The Past
Recaptured

A NURSE IN THE FIFTIES...
AND AFTER

MARY JOYCE BAXTER

Matador
5 Weir Road
Kibworth Beauchamp

ISBN 978 1848761 926

British Library Cataloguing in Publication Data.
A catalogue record for this book is available from the British Library.

Photograph of Presentation of Pingat Jasa Malaysian Medal on back cover
by permission of Genesis Photo Imaging

Typeset in 11.5pt Book Antiqua by Troubador Publishing Ltd, Leicester, UK

Matador is an imprint of Troubador Publishing Ltd

Printed in Great Britain by the MPG Books Group, Bodmin and King's Lynn

To all the nurses, midwives and health visitors with whom I worked and who encouraged me and helped me to achieve success in my chosen career

And to my husband, Arthur, without whose help this book would not have been written

CONTENTS

CONTENTS

PROLOGUE

When I was young, my father used to say to me that the man who married me would deserve a very large medal. He didn't really mean this but he and my three brothers always took delight in teasing me. Nevertheless, the idea that I would never marry because no one would want me was placed in my mind.

This belief was reinforced by my mother who often told me "there are other things in life besides being married". From an early age, I had been aware that my appearance was not attractive and spectacles did nothing to enhance my looks. All the girls of my age I knew were prettier and more self assured.

But I knew a better life must exist for me, and I should try to do something really worthwhile. I did not know, when I made my decision, how horrified my mother would be, and how some in the family would pour cold water on the idea. It was the year 1951 and the Second World War had been over for several years, although rationing was still in place. My job at a printing works was repetitive and boring; the only escape was into books. In those years following the war, and probably due to the deprivation of food rationing, I had been content to drift. Then I realized it was time to shake off the lethargy that threatened to take over and do something more with my life.

Having no certificates to prove my ability and living in a village, transport was limited and night classes were a distance away. My parents, who were old fashioned in outlook even for those days, did not encourage me to go out alone in the evenings and I was shy and self-effacing.

Then I heard that a friend had started to train as a nurse in Birmingham and next time I saw her I asked her about it.

"It will take me three years to become State Registered," she said.

"Do you think I could do it?" I asked.

"It's hard work and not much free time," she said. "You need an application form if you really want to train."

Never having much free time, this did not worry me, "I'd like to try," I said.

"I'll give you the address to write to," she said.

At that time, girls usually stayed at home and if they remained single, found themselves caring for elderly parents. I think this was what my mother expected and perhaps the reason she put me off the idea of marriage.

This future did not appeal so I decided to try this escape route into nursing although knowing my parents would not be pleased. I wrote to the hospital in Birmingham and told my brother George and his wife Joan of my plan.

"They, (meaning our parents) will be quite happy for you to stay at home and be there to look after them," he said, "You go ahead if that's what you want to do. Joan and I will help if we can."

This made me realise there were two choices; one was to stay as I was and do nothing, the other was to take this step into the unknown world of nursing. It was a challenge and I decided to try. A few days later several forms arrived and my mother wanted to know what was in the large envelope making it impossible to keep her in ignorance.

Taking a deep breath, I said, "I want to train as a nurse."

My mother's horrified face revealed her surprise..

"What ever put that idea into your head? You won't like it, you know."

"I've been thinking about it for a while now," I told her.

"But you've got a good job," she said.

"But I'll probably still be doing the same things in twenty years time," I replied. "I want to do something more with my life."

"But *nursing*! You've no idea what you'll have to do!"

"This is an application form," I said.

"I don't know why you want to leave home," she went on, "Throw that form away. Why would they want to take you anyway?"

"If I don't try, I'll never know." I told her and later, carefully filled in the form.

The weeks went by and I wondered if my application had been rejected.

"You won't like nursing," my mother told me repeatedly. "You should put the idea out of your head."

This made me even more determined to go against her advice and wishes. It was a relief when at last a letter came with a date for an interview the following week. So soon after the war, my small, dull, wardrobe was not likely to make an impact but it would have to do.

"I'm coming with you," my mother informed me. This was rather a surprise but I was unable to dissuade her. For a parent to go to an interview with an adult child was unusual and I felt my twenty-three years were quite insignificant.

My mother had never approved of make up and although during the war shortages, this had not mattered, now I felt it did. Surprisingly, my discreet application of face cream and lipstick did not cause any comment and we set off on the day that would

THE BEGINNING

INTERVIEWS

As we travelled to Birmingham on the train, my mother did her best to make me change my mind.

"You'll find it's very different, living away from home."

"Why don't you forget the whole idea and have a day with me at the shops?"

She glanced at the obstinate look on my face and tried again.

"You'll have to do all sorts of nasty things. You won't like it at all."

She didn't realize that the more she tried to put me off the idea of training to become a nurse, the more I was determined to try. As yet, I had no ideas beyond what my friend had told me but I knew that if I did not try, I would regret it for the rest of my life. It seemed that this moment in my life was the ideal time to leave home and do something on my own.

It was a bright October day and winter seemed remote and distant. Perhaps this was an omen of success. However, on arriving at the hospital for the interview and seeing the other candidates my spirits fell. Everyone looked sophisticated and smart compared with what I felt was my own drab appearance. Though they were probably younger, they were self-assured and at ease as if the result of the interview was a foregone conclusion. I was glad my mother had stayed in the reception area for if she had seen the other candidates, she would have more ammunition against my ambition.

Listening to them talking, it was clear most of them had been to high schools and gained a school certificate. Some years before, I had passed the eleven plus examination but because my family had moved from the town on the day of the results, I was not allowed to take my place. Then during the Second World War, things changed and education was not a priority.

Sitting with the other applicants, yet feeling isolated among them made me realise how poorly qualified I was and wonder whether it might be better to give up the whole idea. What ever had possessed me to apply to this hospital knowing so little about what was involved? It was presumptuous to think I could compete with these more qualified women and prepared for defeat even before the interview.

At last, the secretary called me and after giving a timid knock, I entered the Matron's office. A small woman wearing a grey uniform with a frilly white cap perched on her grey hair sat behind a huge desk. Her steely grey eyes looked me up and down as she told me to sit down, continuing to stare at me as I did so. I sat on the edge of the chair to be ready for flight when the inevitable happened and she decided I was not suitable.

"What makes you want to become a nurse?" she asked.

"I want to learn how to look after sick people," I replied, thinking that my reply to this question was not very original.

For several minutes she looked at the papers on the desk in front of her, which gave me time to look around. The room itself did not alleviate the feeling of insecurity, for although it was large, the space was reduced by the number of grey steel filing cabinets around the walls, making it cold, formal and unwelcoming.

Perhaps it was that already being disheartened, my shyness overwhelmed me and I did not give a good impression.

"You are not very big," she remarked in a disparaging tone, "I really do not think you will be suitable for the hard work that nursing entails. It's very strenuous requiring great commitment and study over the three years training."

I did not know what to say to this and as it seemed she had condemned me completely I remained silent. Suddenly, feeling compelled to leave, I started to get up but she waved me back to my seat.

"However," she said. "Because of your lack of qualifications, perhaps you would like to consider training as a State Enrolled Assistant Nurse?"

"I don't know anything about that type of nursing," I said.

"It is less academic with a shorter training than we have here," she said.

This was a possibility I had not known about.

"The course is practical and does not require as much studying," she went on, "I can send you to see someone who can give you more details and arrange an interview at a hospital where you can train. Wait a moment." She lifted the telephone on her desk and spoke into it. "Will you see if you can arrange for a candidate to see Miss Hall?"

I felt indignant at being dismissed without an opportunity to show my capabilities. I wanted to leave the room and go away to forget ever wishing to become a nurse. Then realising it would be stupid to give in at the first set back, at least I should see what Miss Hall could offer.

"Wait outside and my secretary will bring you details."

Even the glimpse of bright sunshine through the windows did not improve the atmosphere as feeling relieved at leaving this forbidding location I went back to the waiting area to wait for the secretary

It seemed a long time as I watched most of the other candidates leave for their interviews and come back to collect their belongings with satisfied expressions, so it seemed obvious that they had been offered a place in the training school. Just as I began to think I had been forgotten my waiting ended as the secretary came in.

"I've been able to make an appointment for you at one this afternoon," she said, it's at Edgbaston." She then told me which bus to get and which stop to ask for. She seemed familiar with this routine and I wondered if this route had been followed by many other would-be nurses. Although at that moment I did not think I had much chance of being accepted, even for training as an Assistant Nurse, to give up at this stage, would be something to regret for the rest of my life.

My mother was waiting in the Reception area and when I told her what had happened she looked at a nearby clock and said. "There's just time to catch the next train home."

It seemed she thought this would be the end of my desire to be a nurse.

"But I want to go and see this Miss Hall," I said.

Her face fell but she insisted we have something to eat before going there.

Although impatient to know what my future might be, we went to a nearby restaurant for we did not know when we might get a train home.

"Would you rather go home?" I asked my mother.

"No, I'll come with you," she replied.

Although not happy about my wanting to become a nurse, she was still determined to stay with me and see what happened.

Following the instructions given to me, we boarded a bus to Edgbaston. The bus stopped close to a large building that the conductor told us, was our destination. Inside, I asked at the Reception desk where we could find Miss Hall. Leaving my mother in a small waiting room, I was directed to the room where I might find out more about my future.

Although I did not know how important a part this interview was to play in my chosen career, I did feel that I must make the most of this chance.

In contrast to the Matron who had interviewed me earlier that day, Miss Hall was dressed more informally in a navy suit with attractively waved dark hair. She looked at me keenly, greeted me in a friendly way and asked me to sit down.

"I hear you want to train as a State Enrolled Assistant Nurse," she said.

My courage had returned during the journey and I answered, "No, I really want to become a State Registered Nurse."

At this, she smiled and asked why.

"I don't want to be pushed into doing something I'm not happy about and I'm sure I'll be able to do the studying and hard work to become an SRN," I replied.

After asking about my education and my present employment, she went on to say, "If it's something you really want to do, are ready to study hard and be willing to do all the difficult jobs?"

"Yes, I will do my best," I told her.

"Then I see no reason why you should not have the chance. I know a matron who might be willing to see you and if she thinks you will make a good nurse, I'm sure she will take you."

Suddenly the atmosphere seemed brighter as I sighed in relief.

Miss Hall explained what the training would involve. Since it was many years ago, I have forgotten all except one part of our conversation.

"Remember," she said, "however hard it gets, and however many times you go off duty despairing of ever making the grade, everyone before you has taken the same training to become a nurse. Staff nurses, Sisters and Matron all have worked just as hard, have shed tears in the sluice and perhaps because of this, have become better nurses."

She went on to say, "The matron who might take you for SRN training won't mind that you have no formal qualifications as long as you are ready to work and study hard. Would you like me to find out if she can see you?"

"Yes, *please*," I could not keep the eagerness out of my voice.

"But I left school at fourteen," I said thinking of the reception I had received at the General hospital.

"It isn't always a matter of previous education," she said and lifting her phone spoke into it. "Will you ask Miss Poole at Selly Oak Hospital if she can see someone who would like to train as a nurse?" She put down the phone and turning to me began to tell me something of what nursing entailed, painting a picture of what life as a student nurse would be. "Yes, it is hard work but there is a lot of satisfaction in seeing someone you have spent time with getting better."

The phone interrupted her and she lifted the receiver, "Yes, she's here in my office. Certainly I'll send her along now."

She put down the phone, "That was Miss Poole, the Matron of Selly Oak Hospital. She will see you at two fifteen."

After explaining how to get there, she wished me success in the future and as I got up to leave said, "remember that everyone who wants to become a nurse has to take the same path. Good luck."

Thanking her, then with a feeling of anticipation that everything was going to be all right, I left her office.

SELLY OAK HOSPITAL

Selly Oak Hospital was not far away so only a short time later we arrived at the hospital gates. As we walked through into the grounds, a porter came out of the lodge.

"Where do you want to go?" he asked.

"I have an appointment to see the Matron," I told him.

"Go through those doors over there and straight along the corridor. The Assistant Matron's office is on the right about half way along. There's a sign so you can't miss it." he told me.

We made our way past colourful flowerbeds to the main hospital entrance where we met a stream of nurses dressed in mauve with white caps and aprons. They were chatting and laughing as they made their way to what, I found out later, was the Nurses Home.

Just inside the entrance hall we found a small lobby in which stood a wooden bench facing out towards the flowerbeds.

It was here that the smell that I soon came to associate with hospitals seemed to pervade the atmosphere, a mixture of disinfectant and possibly ether, something indefinable but not unpleasant.

"I'll wait here for you," my mother sat on the seat and made herself comfortable. "I can look at the flowers and enjoy the warm sunshine while you go and interview the Matron," she said.

"Are you sure you'll be all right?" I asked her.

"Of course. Now don't keep the Matron waiting."

Making my way into the main part of the hospital, I saw a long corridor that seemed to stretch into the distance. On the right, double doors with a notice above them, Ward A1; to the left a door marked Pharmacy with stairs, and another notice that pointed to Wards A3 and A5. I continued along the corridor past 'B' Block and then, seeing a door on my right marked Assistant Matrons. I knocked.

A voice called, "Come in."

The Assistant Matron was tall, slim and quite friendly. She seemed to know all about me.

"Come with me," she said and led me to a small room in which there were several desks and indicated where I should sit.

"Now I want you to answer the questions on this form and then write an essay about why you want to be a nurse."

The questions were not too difficult to answer, mainly about my education and what activities I liked but the essay was more difficult. It is not easy to put into words the reasons you want to learn particular skills. The ideas I had heard the candidates at the General Hospital talk about such as wanting to help other people would not be sufficient to impress.

Then I decided to write a little about myself, about my father who taught First Aid to the girls in the village Guide Company to which I belonged. How I had enjoyed learning something different and could remember so much of what he taught us. Later I had joined the St. Johns Ambulance Brigade to learn more.

The time sped rapidly and it was a surprise when the Assistant Matron came into the room and said, "finish what you are writing and Matron will see you in her office."

Matron's office was light and airy with an uncluttered look although there were several large cupboards on one side of the room. The atmosphere seemed more welcoming than at the General Hospital and I felt at ease straight away. The clear blue sky glimpsed through the window lifted my spirits and seemed like a good omen. Miss Poole was slender and wore a navy blue dress, her cap was edged with broderie anglais. Although she looked me up and down in an appraising manner, I felt she would be willing to give me a chance to show what I could do.

"So you would like to train as a nurse?" she said.

"Yes, if it's possible," I answered as I prepared myself for another rejection.

"I don't see why not," she said. "It is not easy but if you work hard, you can do it. Of course I will check the work you have done and if it is acceptable, arrange for you to have a medical examination. If everything is satisfactory, I will be pleased to accept you in the next student nurse intake."

After she had asked more questions, she said that if she did give me a place she hoped I would work hard and be happy at Selly Oak,

Feeling elated I walked down the corridor to join my mother.

She was sitting in exactly the same spot as when I left her, but I was surprised when she greeted me with the triumphant words," I've seen more of this hospital than you have."

At the incredulous look on my face, she added, "I've been in Casualty while you were interviewing the Matron."

Wondering what might have happened to her, I didn't remind her that it was I who was being interviewed but asked what had happened.

"Well, you had only been gone a few minutes when I felt something on my neck and felt a sharp pain. I'd been stung by a wasp."

Usually my mother was undeterred by wasps and never bothered if she was stung so why did she make a fuss?

"Was it very bad?"

"Oh no, but just as it happened, a nurse was passing and insisted on taking me to Casualty to have it treated. A very nice young doctor put a dressing on for me and gave me some aspirin for the pain."

She had a small dressing on her neck.

"Is it painful now?"

"Not at all. I'm used to being stung as you know but I was looked after so well. They even gave me a cup of tea."

"You were lucky the nurse was there."

"Yes, she said she was late off duty. Do you know she was smaller than you so you won't be the smallest nurse here, that is if they take you?"

"I'll have to wait while the Matron decides about me and I have to have a medical examination to see if I am fit enough."

"She had two stripes on her arm and told me these meant that she had passed her second year exams and had a year to go before she qualified."

My mother had learned more than me about nurse training and would have a topic of conversation for weeks to come.

"Well, let's go and get the train," my mother said. She had forgotten to ask me about my interview but all the way home, she talked about the little nurse who had looked after her.

After this episode, although still not keen about me leaving home, she now seemed to think that if I must go, nursing would not be such a bad career.

Two weeks later, I went back to Selly Oak for a medical and was told by the doctor that I was fit and should have no problems with the physical side of nurse training. It would depend on whether Matron decided that I was a suitable person for all the studying I would have to do.

The weeks went by and I heard nothing at all. Secretly, my mother was pleased for she really did not want me to leave home. My father tended to agree with her but my brother George told me not to worry, these things take time and if I did not get a place at Selly Oak, there were other hospitals.

Christmas day, nineteen fifty one arrived and we were busy preparing our Christmas Dinner when the post arrived. In those days, we had postal deliveries on Christmas Day. Among the Christmas cards was an official envelope from the hospital with my name typed on it.

"Shall I open it for you?" My sister-in-law, George's wife Joan was eager to see what it contained.

I opened it slowly, took a deep breath and took out the official looking document.

"I've got a place." I said, "To start on the sixth of February. There's a list of what I will need to take."

"That's the first hurdle over, it won't be the last but you can do it," said George.

"I have to send measurements for my uniform," I said.

Always eager to help, Joan said, "I'll help you with that."

It was the best Christmas ever and if my parents were disappointed, they did not say so. George and his wife were as pleased as I was.

It was a long time ago, but I have never forgotten Miss Hall, the woman who helped me to take those first steps.

TRAINING

A DAY TO REMEMBER

In complete contrast to the day of my interview, February the sixth was dull and cloudy but even the drizzling rain could not dampen my spirits as I left home.

New students did not have to report until two o'clock at the Woodlands Nurses' Home. Again, my mother decided to travel there with me as she thought it would be a good opportunity to do some shopping in the morning. Father's sister, my Aunt Gladys who lived in Erdington, Birmingham, decided to join us and we met in one of the large department stores.

In the lift, on our way to another floor that morning, we overheard these words, "The King died this morning."

My aunt looked at me and said, "Now we have a Queen."

How sad for the princess who would now become Queen; she had not only lost her beloved father but would soon have the arduous task of being Head of State whilst still grieving. The day became even more important for we were both at the beginning of a new career. It would be harder for her for although the King's health had been poor, no one suspected he would die.

However, following my mother and aunt through the store, I wished the time would pass and my own new life could start. At last, we went for lunch and afterwards to the Bristol Road to get the bus to Selly Oak.

We knew how to find the hospital but not the Nurses Home but the friendly lodge porter directed us further along the road. The Woodlands was a long three-storey building on the boundary of Bourneville in Willow Road. At first sight, it looked rather forbidding, but knowing this was going to be the beginning of my new life, I made my way to the front door. If all goes well, this is where I will spend the next three or four years, I thought and rang the bell.

The door was opened immediately by a large woman in Sister's uniform who introduced herself as Sister Carson, the 'Home Sister'. She would keep her eagle eye on me and all the other nurses for the next few years. I said goodbye to my mother and aunt and followed her into the Nurses Home.

Inside, we passed down a long corridor with doors on either side, then through a door on the right side, which led into a smaller passage. At the end of this, we entered another building where several rooms led from a central corridor. A few doors along, she unlocked and opened a door.

"This is your room for the next three months," she said, giving me the key, "unpack your things, get into uniform and join the others for tea at four."

With this, she left, closing the door behind her and I looked round. On the bed, neatly folded I saw a pile of clothing and looking at this more closely, I found three mauve dresses; twelve aprons and other items that I saw were belts, cuffs, collars and caps.

Sitting on the small chair and gazing around I thought, at last, I'm really here. The room was small but looked comfortable and the wardrobe and chest of drawers were large enough to hold my few clothes.

The sound of voices nearby made me open the door to investigate. At the same time the door next to mine opened and a tall dark girl came out.

We looked at one another and after a few moments, smiled.

"Hello! I'm Margery," she said.

Before I could introduce myself, other doors opened and several others joined us.

Soon we had introduced ourselves and chattered together, finding out a little about each other. There would be seventeen of us starting in what was known then as the Preliminary Training School or PTS for short. Of these, once the first three months had ended, two were to complete their training at the Accident Hospital in Birmingham and two at the Infectious Diseases Hospital in Little Bromwich. The first three months of training would be similar for all of us but after this, we would rarely see these four students except at examinations.

For a while we chatted together until Dilys, a pretty fair haired girl looked at her watch and said, "Don't you think we should get into our uniforms, it's half past three and we'd better not be late on our first day."

We all returned to our rooms to put on our ward dresses and try to make sense of the cuffs, belts and caps. The dress was a pleasant shade of mauve, the white collars, cuffs and belts were stiffly starched. We had three sets of each of these and twelve aprons. The aprons had long straps that were taken over the shoulders, crossed at the back, then fastened neatly under the belt. There was a dark blue, red lined cape that when wrapped well around would keep its wearer warm when walking to and from the hospital.

It was compulsory to wear black shoes and stockings and if laddered, the stockings were to be darned neatly; the shoes had to be kept clean and polished. Only a very little make-up was allowed while on duty and no jewellery of any kind. Nail varnish was not allowed and fingernails had to be kept short. A watch could not be worn but kept pinned in a pocket if it was to be used for pulse taking. For those without a watch, a small instrument rather like an egg timer was useful and these ran for a quarter or half a minute each.

Our finished appearance looked smart and professional and already we were beginning to feel like nurses. The caps were T shaped of a style known as 'Sister Dora' and eventually we were able to fold these so that they looked reasonably presentable. They were kept in place with white Kirby grips that were almost invisible. When everyone was ready, we made our way to the dining room that would only be used on days off; at all other times, meals would be taken in the hospital dining room.

When we had finished our tea, a smart sister dressed in navy blue wearing a 'Sister Dora' cap edged with a frill came in and took us to the study room. At one end a fire burned brightly, otherwise the room contained large tables and straight backed chairs.

As we sat down, she said, "I am Sister Andrews, your sister tutor for the next three months and I'd like to welcome you to Selly Oak Hospital. Today is a day you will always remember, for you are commencing your nursing careers as our new Queen starts her duties as head of this country."

She told us we could study in this room when off duty as there was usually a fire, and our rooms would be cold in winter for there was no central heating in the student's rooms. We found out later that although a fire would be laid ready, we often had to light it ourselves.

"Tomorrow you will have breakfast in the hospital at eight and I will collect you and take you to the Preliminary Training School where you will spend the next three months. At the end of the three months, you will have an exam before you are allocated to your wards."

With this, she wished us well and left us to our own devices for the rest of the evening. After she left, we sat around and talked about the reasons we were there and what had made us decide to become nurses. Most of the others did not have any Educational Certificates; some like me had left school at fourteen.

Several were from Southern Ireland and of these; Bridget and Pat had worked together in a hospital there and wanted to train in England. Although most of the others were about eighteen years old, and one, Bridie, only seventeen, some were older and in their early twenties. However, as Sister Andrews said earlier, no matter what our ages, we would all start equally at the bottom of the ladder that would take us to State Registration.

As we learned each other's names, we discovered that three of us were named Mary and although we would only use each other's surnames on duty, there might be confusion at other times. So my surname, which was then Penlington, was condensed as they decided to call me Penny, a name that has stayed with me for the rest of my life.

I found that some of the others were, like me, apprehensive about taking this plunge into an unknown world. Over the next three years, we would help and support each other and become friends as we shared worries about training and examinations. In addition, at the end of our training, we hoped all would eventually achieve State Registration.

At last, we retired to bed in the part of the Nurses' Home known as the huts, a wooden structure that had been built during the war and was now used for each fresh intake of student nurses.

THE FIRST WEEKS

The bell rang to wake us at half-past six on that first day, as it would every morning for the next three years of our training. There was uncertainty as we donned our uniforms and made our way along Raddlebarn Road to the hospital dining room. The maids were clearing away the remains of the other nurses' breakfasts and had set a fresh table for us.

Despite rationing, the food was surprisingly good and we found no one need be hungry even if for any reason they missed a meal, for there was always bread and margarine for toast and milk for hot drinks available in the Nurses Home.

At ten minutes to eight, Sister Andrews arrived and we followed her out of the dining room, down the corridor and through a side door into the hospital grounds toward the Preliminary Training School. Inside, we were taken into a classroom set out in the familiar way of most classrooms at that time with desks arranged in rows in front of a blackboard.

Those first weeks went quickly as our time was taken in lectures on anatomy, physiology and nursing care. Hygiene was taken by Sister Sigrist, an older tutor whom we all liked. This ranged from learning how to disinfect all sorts of things, types of windows, pasteurisation of milk, water filtration and sewage. There was no time to feel homesick as once out of school we explored the neighbourhood. Further along Raddlebarn road were shops where we were allowed to go in uniform to buy necessities, and beyond these a Catholic church and later I found a small Primitive Methodist Chapel.

The village of Bourneville lay at the end of Willow road and later, when exploring, I found all the streets were named after trees. There was an area of grass like a village green in the centre of the village and when the weather was warmer, it was pleasant to listen to the bells of the Carillon in my off duty time.

One morning Sister Sigrist said, "You are now exactly half way through this course in the PTS and the lectures you need before taking your Preliminary Exams next October." At this, my heart sank for with all the information already received I felt my brain had reached saturation point. How could I possibly learn any more, I wondered, as I went off duty later?

I confided in Ena, "I don't think I can learn anymore!" I said.

Surprisingly, she said, "I feel the same but we have to keep on. We can't give up now."

If anyone else was worried about the work, they did not say anything, so we decided that somehow we must complete the course. Thinking about the reaction of my family if I gave up, I determined to do my best to learn all I could. Strangely after this episode, I found that learning and remembering all I was taught became easier. I reminded myself that everyone at home, with the exception of George and his wife Joan, thought I would be back home for good in a few months so I had to prove them wrong.

A few days later, the rhythm of study began to seem easier and two weeks later, when we had completed well over half the course I felt elated. So much so that on a Friday evening, after a warm sunny day, I walked round the garden humming quietly to myself. That is, I thought it was quiet and to myself until at breakfast the next morning an irate Night Sister exploded into the dining room.

"Who was singing at the top of their voice last evening in the garden and woke me?" she demanded, glaring at us all.

No one spoke; I knew I had not been singing loudly; perhaps it was someone else, so I kept quiet.

"If it happens again I shall send the culprit to Matron." With these parting words she flounced out of the room. Needless to say, none of us dared to walk in the garden in the evening again.

Every Saturday, instead of lectures we were given a two-hour test after which we had a practical demonstration. The test usually consisted of four questions of which we must answer two, taking one hour over each. One Saturday, Sister Andrews was off duty and Sister Sigrist was in charge. The questions consisted of two anatomy, one nursing and one hygiene. We were told to answer any two questions and because the anatomy questions looked more interesting, we all answered those two, ignoring the others.

The following Monday morning, Sister Andrews came into the classroom almost breathing fire and berated us all soundly.

"Why did you all ignore the nursing and hygiene questions this week?"

"We were told to answer any two questions," Margery said.

"You all know that you should only answer one anatomy question. Just because I was away, every one of you took advantage."

"But Sister Sigrist said we could answer *any* two questions," Dilys said.

"All right. But don't do it again."

After this, we heard no more about our error and work continued normally. I learned later, that Sister Andrews had been in the army, which might have been why she was rather a stickler for discipline and order. Later, she told us that if we wanted to join the army, not to become a midwife first. At that time, joining the army was beyond my comprehension and I ignored her advice but did not regret becoming a midwife for I enjoyed work in the Maternity Units of Army Hospitals.

Some of our hygiene lectures were emphasized by visits to places such as a dairy to watch the processes involved in cleansing and sterilising the bottles and pasteurising the milk. Another visit was to the water department where we learned how much of the water to satisfy the needs of a large city was brought from Wales. It was a beautiful day as we walked round one of the reservoirs on the edge of the city.

The last visit was to the sewage works that did not smell as much as we thought. Perhaps this was because it was on the outskirts of the city and a fresh breeze was blowing across from the surrounding hills.

Practical demonstrations consisted of learning to make beds in the approved hospital manner with exact neat corners and wheels pointing in the same direction. This gave a uniform appearance when viewed from the end of the ward. Sister Andrews decided to make them slightly different by putting a small tuck at the bottom of the bed to give the occupant room for their feet to move. This was a good idea from the patient's point of view but when we tried to make them this way on the wards, it was frowned on because the beds looked untidy,

Another important task was the care of equipment and setting up trays and trolleys for all kinds of procedures. We were taught some of these skills with the aid of Mrs. Bedworthy, a large life sized doll who suffered our administrations without a grumble.

One other occupant of the nursing school was Jimmy the skeleton who was used to teach us anatomy, not only to know the names of bones but where each was situated in the human body. Also, the name of every part of each bone and where each was joined to tendon and muscle. I found this aspect of nursing fascinating and because I found it easy to visualize where each bone was placed was able to remember them in exams.

Whilst in school, we were taught the essentials to good nursing practice and always to treat patients with politeness even when they were rude or impolite to us. It was expected that we used their surname unless the patient asked for their Christian or given name to be used. Never, ever to talk about one's personal affairs when treating a patient but to use the time in monitoring the patient's progress and asking them how they felt. Lastly, never to refer to a patient as the bronchitis case in bed eight or repair of hernia in bed two. Always use the patient's name before their diagnosis when referring to them.

One afternoon, Sister Andrews took us to the Hospital Gymnasium and left us in a room wondering why we were there. We did not have long to wait for soon after, a physiotherapist came in.

"Take off your shoes," he ordered.

We looked at each other, wondering what was going to happen.

"In nursing," he explained, "so much of your time in the future will be spent walking up and down the wards for hours. I am going to teach you some foot exercises to help you cope with aching feet. You must practice them every day."

Whilst he was talking, he had taken off his own shoes and sitting opposite us began to demonstrate how we should do the exercises.

These exercises did not seem difficult, but when we came off duty tired and with aching feet, time spent in repeating the exercises made quite a difference.

After a few weeks in PTS, we were given an afternoon off returning after tea at five to be taken to one of the wards where we were instructed to take the temperature, pulse and respirations, (TPR) of the patients. This was our first visit to a ward and I wondered what the patients thought of the invasion of a group of nervous new nurses. Still, they suffered our administrations silently as Sister Tutor's eyes seemed to be on all of us at once. This was the arrangement for the remainder of our time in PTS although we were allowed to perform other tasks as knowledge grew and nervousness diminished.

We were taught the importance of taking the TPR and of how much knowledge we could gain from this about the patient's condition. Depending on the illness, the temperature could change and indicate whether the patient was improving or whether there was a change in their condition. The number counted at the pulse recorded the number of beats each minute but it was only by actually feeling this, that variations in the heart's rate and rhythm could be known and we found that there were a number of changes to record. Respirations may not seem very important but in those days, because of the thick winter fogs or smog, there were many people with respiratory problems giving them difficulty in breathing and the way they managed to inhale. They often had a cough that left them breathless and exhausted and all these had to be reported, first to Sister Tutor and then to the Ward Sister or Staff Nurse. We felt that this was a lot of responsibility and watched our patients carefully whilst we were on the ward.

One occasion, while we were in school, one of the class started to sneeze as if she might be starting with a head cold. Sister Andrews promptly marched us all off to sickbay where she said we would be given a concoction that would get rid of any germs we might have. She was right because after swallowing the mixture, any cold symptoms disappeared completely. No one wanted another dose of this potion that I later learned was called Mist Ammon-Ether, for it had the effect of a bolt of lightning passing through our heads.

During our time in PTS, we finished duty at half past one on Saturday and were not on duty again until the following Monday morning. Because our pay was low, I could only afford to go home about once a month. My mother was pleased to see me and hear about my new life and seemed to be happier about my change of career. Also, because, rationing was still in place, every six weeks, those nurses who could go home were given a stamped ration paper that was equivalent to one week's rations. My mother found this helped augment the family meals which otherwise were stretched when I was at home.

On weeks when I stayed at the hospital, I sometimes visited my cousin who lived at the other side of Birmingham with her husband and two children. At other times, I visited Aunt Gladys in Erdington and took them my weekly allowances of butter and sugar. We had to provide containers and collect these each week from a room on the ground floor. If we were late, often our portions had disappeared.

Time was passing quickly and at the end of our time in PTS, we had an exam to ensure we had learned as much as possible before allocation to the wards.

"I'm sure I won't pass," Norah confided to me that last week.

"Then let's study every night this week," I said.

It seemed that everyone else had the same idea, for each night the study room was full as we asked each other questions. Then at last, the exam which was not as bad as we feared.

Before we were given the papers, Sister Andrews said, "Don't worry, there won't be any questions that you haven't worked on before."

She was right for we had answered similar questions before in class.

On that last weekend, those of us who could, went home, as we were not sure about time off in the future. We were entitled to a half-day and a full day off each week but these might not be together but split through the week.

The four students who were going to the Accident and Little Bromwich Hospitals said goodbye for we would not see them for some time.

At home, my eldest brother Gordon said, "Congratulations for lasting three months. I thought you'd be home in a couple of weeks."

"Well," I replied, "you'd better wait for another three years because I've not really done much actual practical nursing on the wards yet."

"If you finish the course I'll buy you the best present you'll ever have," he said before I left.

Little did he know I would keep him to this for when in March 1955 I did qualify I asked him to buy me a silver belt buckle which I was able to wear when I later became a Sister.

ON THE WARDS

Back in Birmingham, I found I had been sent to Ward C4, Womens' Medical and ENT (Ear, Nose and Throat) with a wide variety of illnesses ranging mainly from heart conditions to diabetes. Everyone told me that Sister Lonerghan in charge was a dragon but as all the other students had been told something similar about the Sisters on their respective wards, I was not unduly worried. Anyway, in my previous occupation, being shouted at seemed to be part of the routine. I decided to do whatever I was asked, work as quickly and efficiently as possible and learn everything they could teach me.

Life on the wards could be extremely hard but I soon learned what to do. Starting with a bedpan round for those patients not allowed up; this finished, all the beds were made, top sheets to the bottom and fresh clean top sheets and pillow cases, or in some cases, clean sheets top and bottom. After this, the beds were pulled into the middle of the ward so the cleaner could clean the floors.

There were two cleaners on each ward, one worked in the morning and the other came in about four in the afternoon and did any cleaning that might be necessary. They both took great pride in their work, as did all the cleaners in the hospital and were part of the ward team. The junior nurses then had to wipe lockers and beds with disinfectant before the beds were pushed back to the wall.

There were two junior nurses, myself and Nurse Brown who was three months senior to me. When one of us had time off, it meant the one remaining on duty had to complete this task alone. Sometimes a second year nurse would help but they had their own busy schedule to complete before the morning break.

Bedpans were kept in the sluice room and were cleaned and disinfected after each use. Urines were also tested there every morning by one of the senior nurses. This room could be quite cold as windows were usually open to dispel any unpleasant smells.

All the wards were of the 'Nightingale' design and there were about thirty-six beds on this ward but on some wards, there could be forty or more. Most wards had side wards, usually one with two beds, the other with four. On admission days, occasionally beds had to be moved to make room for extra patients. No patient was ever left lying on a trolley or in the corridor although occasionally we had to put beds in the centre of the wards as a temporary measure.

On that first morning, it was a relief to go to the dining room but as I began to walk through the door, Nurse Brown pulled me back.

"Never, ever go in front of anyone more senior," she said.

That was a lesson I had to remember, for at that time all other nurses and staff were my seniors; the new intake of student nurses in PTS were junior to me but their mealtimes were different and so we rarely saw them. The Assistant Matrons usually supervised meals and scrutinised us carefully as we walked past. One of them was in charge of our uniform and appearance and made sure all were correctly dressed: anyone who had a button missing or apron straps wrongly crossed was reprimanded. Another Assistant Matron always wore a cap with a bow under her chin; she was strict yet I found that she could be kind.

We were always ready at the morning break to drink coffee and eat rounds of bread covered with dripping.

Back on the ward there were hot drinks to be taken to the patients and bed baths to be done. Then it was dinnertime for the patients and large heated food trolleys were brought up to the wards by the hospital porters.

The ward sister served out the food, allocating what she thought was appropriate for each patient. The nurses carried these to the patients with strict instructions to make sure they could manage to eat and to help any patient who could not. After this, the patients were made comfortable to have a rest and the nurses went for their meal, some at one and others at one-thirty when those who were not then off duty, returned to the ward. Before going to our midday meal, it was the custom to remove aprons, which after a busy morning's work would by then be looking grubby, and put on clean ones.

Over the next weeks, the days flew by so rapidly, it seemed no sooner had we entered the wards it was time to go off duty again. Those first weeks were so busy that we were often too tired when off duty to do anything other than sleep. Of course not everyone had the same off duty time so there might be only one or two other students in my 'set' to join me.

Off duty consisted of one day each week and a half day which could be in the morning or afternoon. On other days, we had two and a half hours off in the morning or afternoon, rarely, in the evening when we finished at five for tea.

With the fresh intake of students in the 'Huts', we were now living in the Main Nurses Home. Most of the rooms were single but there were a few double rooms so some of us had to share: I found myself allocated to a room with Norah, one of the Irish girls, from County Clare.

I was quite surprised to find that although I am only five foot in height, there were several other student nurses who were either the same height or only a little taller. The 'little nurse' my mother had met was even smaller; this did not appear to detract in any way to their skills as nurses.

The work on Ward C4 was demanding but gradually I became used to getting on with my own work and to be ready to help wherever needed. As the days flew by, though my role was very minor, I began to feel part of the team. Quite soon, I found that tasks that might seem unimportant were necessary for the patients' well-being.

Each ward had a 'report' book that gave the patient's diagnosis, information of their progress and any changes in treatment. There was another, known as the 'change' book, where details of each patient's treatment was entered and this had to checked each day. When a treatment was completed, the nurse responsible signed her name. This way everyone knew the tasks that needed to be done and sister knew which nurse was responsible if work was not satisfactory. These treatments such as bed-baths or dressings were in addition to the routine ward work.

Patients who were confined to bed or those who had difficulty in moving had to have their pressure areas rubbed several times a day. This was to prevent pressure sores developing as once the skin was broken, it was painful and treatment became much more difficult.

Every ward had a 'back tray' that was kept specifically for the purpose of treating the pressure areas which included elbows, heels, knees and any area of the back that came into contact with the bed. It was always a good time to chat to the patient whilst treating them and I was often told about their worries and also the highlights in their lives. Some patients were on complete bed rest and prone to develop sores in areas that came into contact with the bed such as heels and elbows. For these patients we made rings of soft material to keep these areas from rubbing and becoming sore.

Very ill patients also had their mouths treated because they were unable to take food and very little to drink. Drinks were encouraged where this was indicated and there was an unspoken rule to give sips of water to these patients as often as possible. The very ill patients had an individual mouth tray on their locker that was used to clean their mouths several times daily but even so, their mouths soon became dry again. These trays had to be cleaned and replenished daily or more often if necessary.

Doing these tasks that today might be called menial helped the nurse to know more about the people in their care. We were taught to treat the 'whole patient' and this is what we tried to do.

Visiting times were strictly adhered to and visitors were given passes to allow them into the hospital; these had to be shown to the Lodge porter before the visitor was allowed to come into the hospital. The hours were seven till eight in the evenings and two until four on Wednesday and Sunday afternoons. No one was allowed to sit on the beds and only two visitors were allowed for each patient although they could change over during the session. Because of this, the wards never got too noisy so very sick patients were not inconvenienced by having too many people around.

Sister Lonerghan *was* strict but would teach as much as she could to any nurse willing to learn and never expected anyone to do something she would not do herself. One day when we were short staffed, I came back from my tea break at half-past four to find she had the trolley set up for bed making.

"Come on, nurse," she said.

"Yes Sister," I said as I joined her.

In all my nursing life, I have never made beds as quickly yet despite the speed, each was perfect and no patient was left uncomfortable. Sister explained to me that there is nothing more soothing for an ill and restless patient than a freshly made clean and comfortable bed.

At least twice a day, the assistant matrons did a ward round with whoever was the senior nurse on duty. Later, as I myself became the senior nurse, I was amazed at how much the senior staff knew about the patients; Matron, when she came to do a ward round was even more knowledgeable about them all and their treatments and progress.

Twice a week on C 4 we had patients, usually children but sometimes adults, who came in for tonsil and adenoid operations. (T's & A's) Every afternoon after their operation, they had to be washed and made comfortable. Often they were still drowsy from the effects of the anaesthetic but I am sure they felt better when their bloodstained faces were washed and they had been changed into clean nightdresses and clean bed linen. They were all reluctant to eat because of their sore throats but Sister made us make sure they did swallow a little soft light food. At the medicine round, they were given a mixture of aspirin suspended in a thick mucilage that was supposed to stick to the throat and soothe the patient's discomfort on swallowing.

One task the junior nurse had to do was to measure and record the urinary output of certain patients and on Ward C4, this was more than half of them. In the sluice, a row of large Winchester bottles stood on a cupboard top, each one allocated and labelled for each patient. Their urine had to be emptied into these and at the end of each day, it was the duty of the junior nurse to measure and empty them, entering the amounts on each patient's intake and output chart. After this, the Winchester bottles were washed and left ready for the night nurse who would repeat the procedure the following morning. These bottles soon became corroded with deposits and were difficult to clean with ordinary soap and water and try as I might I found it impossible to remove the deposits.

One afternoon, after having had a morning off duty, I reported for duty at two. The first task of the afternoon was to make milk drinks for the patients who needed them. I had just put the milk on to heat when Sister came into the kitchen.

"Go down to the sluice and come back and tell me what you see," she instructed.

The sluice room was at the far end of this ward, and wondering why she had given this strange order, I walked down to the sluice room. I remember it so well for it was impossible not to notice the row of Winchester bottles that now sparkled in the rays of sunlight shining through the windows. The grime and deposits had disappeared and now, despite having differing amounts of urine in them they stood proud and gleaming.

"Well! Did you see anything?" sister asked when I returned.

"Yes," I replied, "the Winchesters."

"What about them?"

"It's incredible, I said, "They're so clean and bright."

"Turn off the milk and come with me," sister led me back to the sluice.

"I spent over an hour last night after duty cleaning them," she said. "See that they don't get into that disgusting condition again."

"I'll do my best," I said and wondered how I could.

"This is what I used," she said, lifting a small jar out of the cupboard. It was filled with lead shot.

"Shake some of these around inside the Winchesters with a little disinfectant every time you wash them and they should stay clean."

I murmured a thank you and followed her back down the ward to the kitchen where I continued to make two hourly milk drinks for the gastric patients. As I did this, Nurse Brown who had also been off duty arrived.

Sister looked pointedly at her watch, "You're very late nurse," she remarked scathingly.

Before nurse could apologise, she too was sent down to the sluice.

When she came back Sister asked what she had seen.

"Nothing Sister," she said.

"Go and look again."

Nurse Brown did so and came back.

"What did you see?"

"Nothing Sister."

"Go again and look at the Winchester bottles."

Whilst taking the drinks to my patients, Nurse Brown passed me with a defiant look

"Well?" I heard Sister say in a loud voice.

"They look the same to me as they've always done," the voice was loud.

A moment later, they both passed me on the way to the sluice-room, Sister looking very annoyed. Seconds later they returned and went into the office and raised voices could be heard through the closed door.

Nothing more was said about the incident but with the aid of Sister's 'Magic Balls' as I called them the Winchester bottles were kept clean and gleaming for the remaining weeks I stayed on that ward.

After this episode, although Sister did not overlook my faults, she pointed them out and taught me how to do better and become more efficient.

We had learned about 'last offices' in PTS and when one of our patients died one afternoon I was sent to help another nurse with this. It was the first time I had seen a dead person and did not know what was expected but the senior nurse explained the procedure and showed me what I should do. Everything was carried out quietly and reverently, as we would have done if the patient had been one of our own families...

When all was completed, we rang and asked a porter to take the patient to the North Block. He arrived with a special trolley which had a mauve cover. If the patient had been in the main ward, all the beds in the ward were screened until the patient had gone and the bed was kept screened until it had been disinfected and remade.

Each student nurse had a small book in which was listed all the procedures we should know and be proficient in carrying out before we reached the end of training. At the end of working on any ward or department, this was handed to the Sister in Charge and filled in appropriately. It was quite satisfying to see our books gradually receiving the signatures that denoted we had achieved competence in the correct number of procedures.

NIGHT DUTY

At the end of the first three months we were given two weeks holiday and on returning, I was sent to Ward D1, Womens' Surgical, for a few weeks before going onto night duty. This signalled a change of rooms to the second floor of the Nurses' Home which was quieter and meant having a room to myself. This would be better for studying for the Preliminary Exam which was looming more closely. It was also easier to sleep for the night corridors were kept free from noise.

Sister Smith was a quiet pleasant person who was always ready to explain about the patients in her care. The ward routine was very similar to C4 but the patients and their treatments were quite different.

One afternoon, an eighteen-year-old girl was admitted with severe abdominal pain; the doctor examined her and diagnosed acute appendicitis that meant she needed an operation. I tried to reassure her as I helped her change into an operation gown and long woollen stockings. I tied a triangular bandage over her hair and then one of the senior nurses came to give her a pre-medication injection. This made her drowsy and when the theatre porter arrived to take her to the emergency theatre she was almost asleep.

Taking a patient to theatre for the first time was a new experience and although wanting to see more of this aspect of nursing, it was impossible to know what to expect while waiting with her in the anaesthetic room.

Everything seemed to be going well on the operating table, her skin was swabbed and the area covered with sterile towels when suddenly, she moved.

This shocked and dismayed me, as I thought she was not completely under the effects of the anaesthetic. The look in my eyes must have shown how this had startled me for the anaesthetist reassured me that these were involuntary movements and did sometimes occur.

Later, when she recovered from the effects of the operation, I went to wash and help her change into her own nightdress before her visitors came.

I asked, "Do you remember what happened?"

"I remember being wheeled along the corridor and then waking back here."

It was a relief to know she had not wakened during the operation. Since then, there have been horrendous stories of people being awake and knowing what was happening but, because of the drugs they had been given, unable to do anything about it.

After operations, some patients had difficulty in passing urine and various strategies were used to overcome this. Quite often, putting screens round the bed and turning on nearby taps would be sufficient. If this failed, I found that pouring warm water over the lower abdomen often helped. It was only very rarely that a catheter needed to be used.

Although the main doors of the Nurses' Home were locked at ten every night, one could ask permission for a 'late key' that meant one need not be in until ten thirty. Even today I remember the strident voice of the Home Sister walking round the nurses home calling, "Anyone want a late key?"

Before being given the key however, it had to be approvd by one of the Assistant Matrons.

Two weeks after returning from holiday, I spent my first night on this busy surgical ward. It was not easy at first for acute cases were often admitted at night and some had to be taken to the operating theatre. We were supposed to work for five nights and have two nights off but often we had to work more nights than this and still only had two nights off but at the end of our session those nights owing to us were made up when night duty ended.

When on night duty, staff were supposed to be in bed by eleven in the morning but I was usually so tired, I went straight to bed when I came off duty.

After nights off, we had to be back and in bed by two to sleep in preparation for being on duty all night. It took a while to get used to this change in routine but it was always difficult to sleep in the afternoon after returning from nights off.

Most nights, the senior on this ward was Nurse Stringer, a third year nurse, who I heard later, had failed her finals and was waiting to retake them.

Many patients had operations during the day, so about two in the morning when their post-operative sedation wore off, they were often very uncomfortable. It was routine procedure, when these patients woke, for the night staff to wash them and change their bed linen after which a repeat sedative was given to ease their discomfort. This procedure was carried out very quietly so as not to disturb the other patients. It meant that when the day staff came on in the morning, these patients could rest quietly until their next sedation was due.

Some patients were restless at night but there was a supply of Ovaltine, Horlicks or Cocoa available to help induce sleep once more. Some were in constant pain and it could be extremely difficult to make them more comfortable.

At that time, many elderly women came in with a broken neck of femur and the treatment was to place the limb in a Thomas splint and apply traction to this. Healing often took many weeks but remaining in a static position did not help them and very often, they would succumb to pneumonia and die. It was always difficult to treat their pressure areas in this position but this did make them a little more comfortable. We did our best to alleviate their discomfort but it was difficult and I wished it was possible to do more for them. Nowadays most patients with a broken femur are taken to theatre and the bones are pinned. Then quite soon after this, the patients get up and are allowed home.

Although often busy at night, sometimes there was time during the quiet hours to listen to a sleepless patient's problems and though not always able to help, perhaps talking helped them to find a solution.

There were several patients I remember. Miss Jordan who had gallstones and lived a short distance away in Acacia Avenue; Mrs. Mason who had a spinal operation and who was with us for quite a long time; there was also Allie, a young girl in her teens who following poliomyelitis was almost completely paralysed. She was with us for several months and was bright and optimistic though her life must have been very difficult as she had only slight movement in one arm and could not move the rest of her body. Months later, when no longer on the ward, I heard she had died from kidney failure and felt sad that her too short life had ended.

On busy intake nights, sometimes another junior nurse was sent to help and on several nights, Nurse Denver came to us but she was not well, disappearing quite often to the sluice where she was very sick. Later, I learned that she was pregnant and had to leave but that Matron had done what she could to help her.

Although very strict about patient care, Miss Poole, the Matron, was kind and considerate to any nurse who had problems.

Night Sister visited the ward at least three times during the night when the senior nurse walked round the ward with her and gave her an update on the patients' progress. No one ever did a ward round with their arms folded but had their hands clasped behind them. This way, it was easier to be ready to help a patient if needed. Having folded arms tends to give an impression of being aggressive. No one ever chewed gum whilst attending to a patient or doing a ward round with a sister or Matron. It was also important to wear one's cuffs when accompanying a senior nurse or a doctor on a ward round. As most of our work was done with sleeves rolled up, it could be difficult to get our cuffs which were usually left in a kitchen drawer. In this case, frantic signals were made for someone to bring them. Once, when this happened to me, a rather large size was brought causing me to hold my small wrists rigid for fear they would slip off onto the floor.

Whilst Night Sister was on the ward, the junior nurse stood near the phone in the corridor ready to respond quickly if it should ring and disturb the patients. There was a system of lights on all the corridors, red, blue, green and white and combinations of these, either stationary or flashing were used to notify the doctors if they were needed. If a doctor was on the ward, the junior nurse needed to know which lights were for him or her and could then take a message. This system of finding personnel did not disturb the patients as a ringing phone might when not answered immediately.

One night, Sister had just left when the phone rang and a man's voice asked if Nurse Benson was there. I replied that no, she was not on this ward and he rang off. When I told the Senior Nurse, she laughed and said. "That must have been Doctor Taylor, he gave me that name as he knows I smoke Benson and Hedges. He must have run out of cigarettes and wants one of mine."

Later, I met Doctor Taylor who proved to be lively and friendly and being a junior houseman, he spent a lot of time in the hospital at night.

In the morning, the Senior Nurse wrote a report that was taken to the office. A copy of this was written in the Ward Report Book for the ward sister or staff nurse when they came on duty at eight. The Senior Nurse also did a ward round with the Sister or staff nurse and gave a verbal account of the patients' conditions. In this way, the Sister knew exactly how the patients were and could organise their nursing care.

The morning was the busiest time especially for junior nurses who soon became used to getting on with the chores whilst the senior nurse wrote her report. So it came as a surprise when one morning, the senior nurse came onto the ward to help me. This was not at all usual but I found that Nurse Carr always helped when she could and I looked forward to the two nights she spent on this ward each week. It made quite a difference to see her friendly face as some of the senior nurses distanced themselves from the juniors and rarely if ever helped with the morning chores.

When we went on duty in the evening, we were given breakfast and had what would have been our midday meal any time between midnight and two in the morning depending on how busy we were. Then when we went off duty, we had supper which seemed at first, a rather topsy-turvy way of things but in time we got used to it. During meal times, one or other of the night sisters would be present to keep an eagle eye on us.

Arriving one evening for breakfast, I did not feel well and ate only a little cereal, hoping that the sister would not notice. Unfortunately, she had, so when one of the other night sisters came to the ward, she said.

"I hear you are not feeling well."

By this time, having completed my chores, I felt better and said, "Yes I did not feel well when I came on duty but I feel much better now."

She looked at me and said, "You do look rather pale. The ward is quiet so go to sick bay, slip into a bed and rest for a while."

The sick bay was quiet and I removed apron, cap, shoes and dress, slipped between the cool sheets, and was soon asleep.

At five in the morning, someone came to wake me and I went back to the ward feeling much better. This showed how the senior staff observed and looked after the health of the nurses in their care.

One night, Nurse Stringer and I were talking about exams. She told me that unfortunately, she had failed her Finals twice and was really worried as if she did not pass the next time, she would have to leave.

"So far," I said, "I've passed all my tests so I'm hoping I'll pass the Prelims."

"Did you use the same pen you have there?" she asked.

"Yes, my brother gave it to me before I came here."

The pen was a blue Waterman fountain pen that I enjoyed using and which produced writing that looked well although my handwriting was not good.

"Can I borrow it for my finals?" she asked.

"As long as I don't need it on that day," I said.

After several months of night duty, the students in my set were moved onto days, as the first of our nursing exams was due. Before this, we had some revision study days with the students from the set before ours who would be taking the same examination. This time however, we did not return to the PTS but went to the Nurse Training school, a larger building with a Senior Tutor, Miss Brun, in charge. Through most of our training, our Tutor was Sister Partington and I shall always be grateful for her help and encouragement throughout my training.

At last the day came for this first exam which consisted of written papers on Anatomy, Physiology and Hygiene. We were glad when this was over but worried whether we had answered our questions correctly. Sister Tutor told us we should not worry as we had good grounding in these subjects in PTS and had answered similar questions previously.

As the written work for the final exams was on a different day, Nurse Stringer appeared and reminded me of the promise made on night duty. Later, she returned my pen saying that she had good feelings about the exam this time.

.Several weeks later, the results arrived and most of my set had passed and so were ready to go on to Part Two of the Preliminary Exam. This would take place the following February and consisted of a paper on Nursing Practice and a Practical Exam. I was happy when Nurse Stringer came to say she had passed.

"Keep that pen safe," she said, "it's lucky."

The pen meant more to me because it was a gift from my brother but I also thought that studying had a lot to do with passing exams.

Meantime we had been allocated to wards on day duty and my destination was Ward A5, Womens' Medical where although still a junior nurse, there were now two new intakes of students who were junior to me. This meant performing tasks that were more senior and at other times, junior nurse's duties. In this way, the knowledge already gained was reinforced, giving realisation that being able to do the menial tasks as well as the more important ones was what being a good nurse really meant.

In charge of this ward was Sister Boston, who could be moody, so most of us found it better to get on with our work and keep out of her way if we could.

One task was testing urine, which was then so different to the way it is done now. A row of specimen glasses stood in the sluice room every morning, each containing urine from the patients. It was not possible to hurry even though the room was cold. First, the specific gravity was taken and the acidity tested with litmus paper. Sister Tutor taught us a jingle to help remember this.

'Red to blue, alkaloo,
Blue to red, aced.'

After this, the specimen was boiled by holding it over a Bunsen burner to test for protein, a sure way to get one's fingers burned as often there were no test tube holders available and we had to do the best we could to hold the tube over the flame. It was then tested for sugar by adding a special tablet to the urine which reacted with the specimen and heated it making it hot so once again, the unwary nurse could burn her fingers and sometimes drop the tube.

This was a disaster as test tubes were in short supply and breakages had to be reported to sister. If sugar was present, when the fizzing subsided the resulting colour would range from green to bright orange.

Other tests were also completed and the results noted in a book for sister to see and marked on the patients' charts. This process could take a lot of time but there was no way it could be hurried. Some of the patients' urine, especially the diabetic ones, had to be tested more frequently. The dose of insulin given to the patient was decided by the amount of sugar in the urine and the sister or staff nurse would check this.

The consultant doctor on this ward was a polite gentleman and I found that Dr. Taylor who was now doing his Medical internship was his houseman.

THE FIRST CHRISTMAS

The months passed quickly and soon it would be Christmas for which preparations started early. Every year, the nurses held a concert and that first year, an adaptation of Disney's Alice in Wonderland was to be performed and as many as possible were encouraged to take part. I was given the part of one of three rabbits after an audition and for this I had to sing the following verse:

I'm late, I'm late
For a very important date
No time to say hello. Goodbye!
I'm very, very late.
And so you see,
I'll have my cup of tea
Behind the kitchen door
When no one's there to see.

The other 'rabbits' sang a similar song with variations to fit in with aspects of hospital life that no one was supposed to know about. The main theme of the play was about a student nurse who wanted to wear the blue dress of a staff nurse. Naturally, in the end she achieved this ambition.

'In her sweet little Alice blue gown,
She strolls up the ward and then down.
Though the students may bore her
The patients adore her
In her sweet little Alice Blue Gown.'

This was enacted in front of any other students who were off duty and other invited friends. Everyone enjoyed this performance even though by today's standards perhaps it would seem amateur. After our performance, the junior doctors had their turn and put on a parody of Cinderella. This was about a prince (the obstetrician) who was looking for a woman with the perfect pelvis. Everyone enjoyed this even the obstetrician laughed as they mimicked the way he walked when demonstrating the difference between white European and native women. This he had said made all the difference in how they went through labour.

The highlight for many of us was Christmas Eve. Any off duty nurses joined in carol singing and all met at the entrance to the hospital.

A senior nurse said, "Turn your cloaks inside out," and we all did as instructed, some taking a lantern to hold aloft as we walked two by two following her through the main door to the wards.

Starting at the childrens' Ward A1 we started to sing. "Away in a Manger" was the first carol, then on through other carols as we made our way through A3, A5, up and down stairways and across the bridges that joined the ward blocks together, to B block and then C and D blocks, singing as we went.

One moment we were walking through the warm wards, the next, out in the open with the cold December wind blowing so that we pulled our cloaks tightly around our shivering bodies.

When at last it was over, most of us made our way to the Nurses' Home for a well-earned rest. For many, nurses and patients alike, it was the first Christmas away from home but singing Carols helped make us feel closer to our families.

Each Sister decorated her ward at Christmas and chose various themes and subjects to celebrate the festivities. All the work was completed by the ward staff in 'off duty' time yet no one complained about this; we wanted to give the patients as happy a Christmas as we could.

On duty early next morning, those on duty shared the routine tasks, and then most importantly, all the patients were made comfortable, and if allowed, were given mince pies with their morning drinks.

A sudden noise outside the ward made everyone turn towards the doors where the porter from Pharmacy was sitting on his trolley with a little harmonium, playing with gusto a melody of popular songs interspersed with carols. One of the other porters pushed the trolley into the ward to the delight of the patients. Luckily, in the main ward none were very ill so were able to enjoy this interlude. Those in the side wards also seemed to enjoy the music which was muted by closed doors.

For some reason, Sister Boston was not in a very good mood and when the porters had gone, began to find fault with the nurses. We were sent around the ward to tidy the already neat beds, while she complained that she had never known such untidy nurses. That morning, several of us felt despondent which was not good as it was admission day for the ward.

I was not the only nurse near to tears as I walked out of the main ward where I was met by Doctor Taylor. He grabbed me and said no one should be unhappy at Christmas and if they were, he had the remedy. At this he pulled me into one of the side wards where he had previously hung some mistletoe and to the amusement of the two patients there kissed me. He proceeded to cheer us all up by finding another piece of mistletoe and chasing nurses into corners where he made full use of it.

"Now I've only to catch Sister and put her in a good mood," he said as he departed into the office. I do not know what happened but Doctor Taylor certainly had a way of getting on her good side and for the rest of that day, Sister was in an amiable mood.

At lunchtime, the consultant arrived on the ward to carve the turkey while Sister organised its distribution to the patients. After this, the nurses made sure that the patients were comfortable and could rest whilst the staff went in relays for their own meal. At two, the visitors arrived and then at three, the ward doors were opened and a piano wheeled into the main ward. I recognised one of the Pathological Laboratory technicians and his wife who then sang a variety of popular songs ending with 'We'll gather Lilacs' so beautifully rendered that tears were in many of the patient's eyes.

During this time, the everyday ward work continued as usual so that by evening, we were glad to see the night nurses appear. Most of us were ready to go off duty as everyone had been working on the ward all day and we had admitted several ill patients.

The following day, the usual routine returned and the day after Boxing Day, all decorations were removed and by the end of the week, we had almost forgotten the festivities.

In the New Year, we began to study for the second part of the preliminary examination that took place in February. For this, we had a paper on Nursing Care and also a Practical Examination. Sister Partington our Tutor told us not to worry too much about this as we had all had enough experience in ward work to be able to pass.

Despite this, I still felt rather nervous and made the mistake when asked to prepare a kaolin poultice of making one large enough for someone's chest when a much smaller four inch square one would have been adequate. Nevertheless, with most of the other students, I passed this exam. Following this and having passed the hospital First Year exams, we became Second Year Nurses and were able to sew a stripe on our ward dresses. This caused some teasing from the patients, especially on the men's wards where we were often addressed as lance corporal when out of Sister's hearing.

This meant that I had now completed one year of training and I also gained a prize for coming top in the hospital exams. Looking back over the months, in spite of the hard work and unpleasant tasks I often had to do, I realised that taking this step to become a nurse was the best thing I had ever done.

THE SECOND YEAR

Many of the Sisters had their own particular preferences in the treatment of their patients, on B 1 for instance, the Sister liked all the men after an operation to have their chests rubbed back and front with camphorated oil. This helped the men to find their breathing was easier as the vapour was inhaled. It also had the side effect of leaving one's hands beautifully soft.

Now as second year nurses, we had more responsibility and part of this was to make sure the junior nurses were able to do their work correctly. A few weeks before the time came for the Queen's Coronation, I was sent to Ward D3, a ward where those of my friends who had worked there, said the Staff Nurse was very strict. This ward was virtually ruled by Staff Nurse Cox but on discovering that by arriving on duty promptly she was not the ogre I'd been dreading. She was an extremely good nurse and taught me a great deal about the practical basics of nursing care.

One day, another nurse and myself had bed bathed a patient, changed her sheets and made her as we thought, comfortable. Staff Nurse came to see the patient when we had finished and asked her, "Are you comfortable, Mrs. Brown?"

"Yes Staff," was the reply.

Staff gave her a quizzical look and turned to me with a shrug.

"Don't just stand there, give me a hand, nurse," she said.

In moments, whilst supporting the patient we removed the pillows from behind her head and shook them, and then Staff Nurse replaced them carefully.

"How's that?" she asked.

"Oh, much better," was the reply.

Although to my inexperienced eyes, the patient had looked comfortable, after Staff Nurse Cox had finished I could see a change in the way the patient now appeared. It was watching and learning from this experienced nurse at work that helped me improve my nursing skills. Although I found working with her could be quite exhausting, I was sorry when the time came to leave the ward.

While on this ward, I went to admit a patient with Sister. This young Irish girl was bleeding heavily; she was having a miscarriage and must have been in considerable pain. I prepared the frightened Irish girl for theatre and tried to do my best to make her feel better. At that time, many of these girls had what was known as a 'back street' abortion' an illegal act that very often went wrong.

As a second year nurse, another skill in which to learn competence, was to give injections. Although we had been taught this as junior nurses, we had not been allowed to give these alone. All drugs had to be checked by the Staff Nurse or Sister before being given under supervision. When satisfied that we were capable of doing this, we were allowed to give them on our own. All dangerous drugs, including those given orally had to be checked by a registered nurse. Giving a first injection was an ordeal but in time we became used to doing this as quickly and painlessly as possible.

The block opposite D3 was D4 where those mothers from the obstetric unit upstairs who had Caesarean sections were nursed. Sister Ball was in charge and often called on one of D3 nurses to help and often, that nurse would be me; I did enjoy looking after the babies, soon becoming used to Sister's ways.

On the twenty-ninth of May, we heard the news that Hilary and

Tensing had reached the summit of Mount Everest, just in time to make the events of the following week even more special. Everyone was interested in the preparations that were going on in London for the Queen's Coronation. How we wished we could be there among the cheering crowds but we would have to hear the commentaries on the radio and see the pictures in the newspapers. Many patients had to stay in hospital for several days after an operation so they would not be able to join in the festivities.

Then the husband of one of the longer stay patients had an idea which he put to the ward sister. He offered to bring in a television and set it up in the ward so that as many patients as possible could see the coronation. Sister agreed to this and so on June the second, as many patients who were able, were made as comfortable as possible in bed or chairs arranged round the television to enjoy watching the new Queen being crowned. It was a small black and white set but everyone was enthralled by the wonderful spectacle.

Of course, the nurses had to continue with their individual tasks as dressings and treatments had to be done and patients made comfortable. No one wanted to go off duty but wanted to stay and watch. Sister agreed as long as they helped with any essential work.

Ward D4 was unusually busy that day and Sister Ball kept calling me to help with the babies and new mothers. Despite this, on the occasional quick visits to D3, I was able to take a quick look at what was going on in London. Glimpses of the Queen in her coach made the day special. The never to be forgotten sight of Queen Salote of Tonga in an open carriage waving and smiling despite the rain was a highlight too.

The following month, the Nurses Prize giving took place and I was happy to be given the First Year prize.

SECONDMENT

Not long after this, in July nineteen fifty three, I was seconded to the Infectious Diseases Hospital at Little Bromwich for two months. This was completely new to me but whilst there I learned how Barrier Nursing of infectious patients should be carried out.

Outside each cubicle was a washbasin beside which hung a barrier gown. Before donning the gown hands were washed, only after this the cubicle could be entered and any procedures carried out. After leaving the patient, the nurse's hands were washed again, the gown removed, folded with the outside in, replaced on the hook, then hands washed again. It was important that this procedure was followed rigorously but it took much more time so I was glad there were not many patients on this ward.

That there was no cross infection on the wards, where this procedure was carried out efficiently, was evidence that this practice was effective.

It was good to meet the two nurses who were in PTS with me and catch up on their news. Unfortunately, I did not see as much of them as I would have wished because after only two weeks, I was transferred to night duty.

Unlike my own hospital, I found only one nurse on each ward to do everything needed. The ward I was sent to at first was adult with a variety of illnesses. One man had developed Poliomyelitis whilst on honeymoon; this had left him with weakness in one arm which fortunately the doctors thought might only be temporary. In another cubicle, a man from Jamaica had Diphtheria and needed to be given a calculated dose of gamma globulin at intervals throughout the night. He must have hated to see me with my tray to give him this injection.

All patients' cutlery and crockery was kept separately and boiled after use in a huge fish kettle in the ward kitchen.

One evening as we prepared to go on duty, one of the other night staff said, "Sister Elizabeth Dixon is due back from holiday today. This meant little to me until a new sister arrived on my ward later that night. It was difficult to know which of us was more surprised when we recognised each other. We had been good friends when attending school together and although the same age as me, she had already become State Registered in both General and Fever Nursing. Betty, as I had known her, emphasised that I should not show any familiarity or call her Betty in front of the other staff. As it happened, I saw very little of her whilst there and I never knew what happened to her after I went back to Selly Oak.

All the wards were in separate blocks with areas of lawn in between so to visit all of them took the Night Sister some time. One rode a bicycle between the wards so that she could do her rounds quickly. An unforgettable sight was seeing her on a wet, windy night battling with an umbrella as she cycled through the hospital grounds.

The ward opposite to mine was a children's ward where all of them had whooping cough, a disease prevalent at that time. All night, I heard the children coughing and the nurse on that ward hurrying between them to try to relieve them. During the day, I often woke up thinking I could still hear those distressed children and wondered why I was not there to help them.

While I was at this hospital, I went home on my day off and brought my bicycle back. This proved to be very useful for when it was fine, I was able to ride around the neighbourhood and it was the means of cycling to Evesham where my grandfather, aunt and uncle lived and this saved on bus fares.

A week later, I was sent to another children's ward where there were several children who needed regular medication. It was emphasised that medicines should be given on time to give the child the full benefit of treatment. Where possible, this was arranged so that their sleep was not disturbed too much.

As there was only one nurse on each ward, some procedures had to be done alone, even though it might be better to have another nurse to assist. On one particular night, I had to give a little boy an injection of Penicillin. Usually I had no trouble, as the child was not nervous about this. When told what was about to happen, normally he would lie quietly until the injection was finished. This night however, he was startled at a sudden noise outside the ward, just as the injection was completed. The syringe was knocked from my hand and flew into the air. Retrieving it from where it had fallen I discovered the needle had broken. Looking carefully in his leg and in the bedclothes with the help of a torch there was no sign of the missing piece of needle. I rang the Night Sister to tell her what had happened and we both looked everywhere we could. By this time little Tom was fast asleep and Sister decided there was not much we could do until morning when we might be able to see better. It was a great relief later when I went to make Tom's bed and found the needle stuck in one of his blankets.

Soon after this, my secondment ended and I went back to Selly Oak where we were about to start our second year lectures.

LATE KEYS AND LECTURES

At this time, the 'block' system of lectures was used in many hospitals; a method which took the nurses off the wards for two or three weeks to attend lectures. At Selly Oak, the practice was to have a weekly study day over several weeks. This method suited me as we had a week in between each study day in which to write up notes and read more on the subjects of our lectures.

One of the surgeons gave us lectures on Surgery and the consultant from Ward A5 lectured in Medicine. Dr Norton held our attention effortlessly and described illness so well that the subject matter came to life and seemed easier to remember. Later, in examinations, his lectures were a great help.

About this time, Matron Poole retired and a new Matron was appointed in her place. Miss Brown was a pleasant lady, a strict disciplinarian but also kind so that if we worked and studied hard and did not neglect anything we had nothing to fear from her. The myth of the Matrons who were 'battle axes' did not seem to apply to our matrons. However, this did apply to a deputy Matron who came to work at the hospital for several months. Everyone went in fear for a glance from her could send shivers through a nurse and make her wonder if she had done anything wrong. She did not stay long but moved to become Matron of a busy hospital in the North of England. We all felt sorry for the nurses at this hospital. Several years later, I met a nurse who had trained at this hospital and who assured me that all the students had feared this Matron.

Evenings off were rare; the only occasion when my 'set' were off together was after a study day when we often went to the cinema. The nearest was on the Bristol Road but as funds were limited, we could only afford the cheapest seats. These were always near the front, which meant we had to sit with our heads well back to see the screen.

Sometimes, on an evening off there was time to visit my Aunt Gladys who lived in Erdington, another part of Birmingham. Usually I took one bus to the city centre, walked through the town to get another bus to Slade Road in Erdington where she lived. One evening, after a pleasant chat, I got up at nine to go and get the bus back but Aunt Gladys said,

"Why not get the Circular bus. It will save going through the town centre."

Foolishly, I agreed, as even in those days, walking through Birmingham town centre was not something to be desired. It was so much easier to walk the short distance up the road to the bus stop. There was not long to wait for buses were frequent and usually on time. I sat back prepared to enjoy the journey but as my watch revealed, time was rushing past, it was almost ten and we were still a long way from my destination.

Realising I was going to be late, the full wrath of Home Sister would descend on my head. No good to try and explain what had happened for she would not listen but berate me for not having the sense to know that a bus would take longer to travel around the outside of the city. There was no possibility of trying to get into the Nurses' Home through one of the downstairs windows. The rooms on the ground floor in the Nurses' Home had sash windows that could be opened only about two or three inches from the bottom and although they could be opened further from the top, it would be impossible to get in this way, as they were far too high.

Why couldn't the bus go faster? Why were so many people getting on and off at each stop? Why had I been such an idiot, I thought, as the time hurried by?

I felt agitated, knowing Home Sister would not believe my excuse and send me to Matron.

In my mind, I could hear her words, "As a second year nurse you should have more sense."

Was it possible that I might be sent home in disgrace for breaking rules?

Yet there was nothing I could do, just sit on the bus and hope it would not be too late. There was a possibility that I might be able to sneak in with someone else who did have a key. Then as the bus stopped yet again to let on more passengers, I realised it would not even be there before ten thirty. Then a familiar figure got on the bus and sat down a few seats in front. It was Sister Partington our tutor so when I saw a vacant seat next to her, I moved up the bus and sat beside her to tell of my predicament.

"I'm afraid I'm going to be in trouble," I said.

"Why, whatever's wrong, nurse?"

"I've been to see my aunt in Erdington and she persuaded me to get the Circular bus but I was stupid not to realise that it would take so much longer than going into the City centre and then out to Selly Oak."

"You *are* going to be late I'm afraid. Do you have a late key?"

"I'm afraid not. I've never needed one before but even if I had one, I would still be late."

She smiled at this and said, "Don't worry. You can come in with me and if we do meet Home Sister, I will deal with her."

As it happened, we did not meet Sister Carson although we heard her voice in the distance talking to someone. I was able to slip quietly upstairs to my room having had a narrow escape and would make sure it did not happen again.

At the end of the second year we had another exam and those of us who had passed were allowed to add another stripe to our uniform dress.

More night duty and this time we were often in charge of the ward and remembering my own first night duty, I tried to help and encourage the junior nurse whenever possible. Some of the time was spent on B 2, Male surgical and orthopaedic and because the work could be heavy, a male orderly worked with us most nights. Dennis never seemed to mind how much he had to do. Being Irish, he had a touch of the blarney, often the night sister would leave the ward smiling at his remarks. One night he greeted one of them with, "Good evening Sister Honeybunch," a corruption of her name which could not be unnoticed.

Many of the patients were healthy young men who had been involved in accidents, most sustained whilst playing football. It was difficult for them to be immobile for long and they often tried to get up, an exercise that usually ended in disaster. Dennis was often called on to help them get back into bed, as most were too heavy for the nurses to lift.

Another incident occurred one morning; the beds had just been tidied when the senior Night Sister who was known as Dido came to do her round. At the far end of the ward, were four Balkan Beam beds, two on each side of the ward. These were where men who had fractured legs were in traction to keep the broken bones apart whilst healing took place. They were rather like huge four posters and blocked the view to the entrance to the ward.

As Sister entered the ward, the men suddenly started singing, 'Onward Christian Soldiers' as loudly as only men who were fit and healthy despite their injuries can sing. At this Sister turned and walked out of the ward looking furious but came back later to give the culprits the sharp end of her tongue. I never knew whether the men had intended this escapade or whether someone had given them a signal but Sister was decidedly frosty with staff and patients alike for several days.

INCIDENTS DURING TRAINING

Whilst on night duty, it was decided to decorate the Nurses Home and so all nurses on night duty were transferred to another Nurses Home. This was to prevent them from being disturbed by all the activity. Having been built during the war to accommodate those training as State Enrolled Assistant Nurses, the rooms were small. These rooms were only about six feet wide and eight feet long so had been nicknamed the 'horse boxes'. Each room contained a bed, a small chest of drawers and a tiny wardrobe. There was hardly enough room to turn round and I was glad to be moved back to the Woodlands.

The concert hall was in the same building and every Sunday morning, the Roman Catholic Priest came there to celebrate Mass for there were quite a number of Catholic nurses.

One Sunday morning I came off duty and went to the bathroom but on returning to my room my key would not unlock the door. However hard I tried, it would not turn. I was in a dilemma as it was quite a cold frosty morning and went to find the Sister in charge but she too was in the Concert Hall waiting for Mass to begin. I asked someone to tell her of my problem but either she could not or would not come out. Luckily, a friend let me stay in her room until I could get help. When the Home Sister appeared, she sprayed the lock with oil and then it opened easily. It appeared that all the locks tended to seize up at times and I dreaded a reoccurrence.

After coming off night duty, I was sent to Ward F Children's

Medical. This Ward and Ward L, the other children's Medical ward were each in separate blocks in the hospital grounds and were always busy but the work was interesting and the children rewarding to care for.

Some of these children had chronic conditions which meant a long stay in hospital and they seemed to know everything that went on in the hospital. Even so, it was surprising to hear Mark, a young boy with Still's Disease, (juvenile arthritis) telling the other children that the porters had just taken a 'stiff' to the mortuary. How did he know that the mauve covered trolley held a dead body? It was difficult to be cross with him for he was always brave despite being in constant pain.

It was whilst being in charge on this ward one afternoon, one of the Assistant Matrons came to do a round. I remembered all the diagnoses of the children but when I came to a new child told Sister Davis that she had been admitted with PUO.

"And what is that nurse?" she asked.

My mind went blank and I could not remember what PUO meant so said, "Pain of Unknown Origin,"

"Are you sure?" she said.

"Yes," I replied.

As soon as the ward door closed behind her, I realised what I had done. I should have said, Pyrexia of unknown origin so no wonder Sister Davis had given me a quizzical look when she left.

I told Sister about this when she came back on duty.

"I feel such an idiot," I said.

"Don't worry about it," she said. "No harm has been done and the correct diagnosis will be in the evening report."

In the Nurses Home, most of the mattresses on our beds were hard and not very comfortable. Being tired after a long day on duty, we did not really notice this. During my second year, these mattresses were gradually replaced with new spring mattresses; in time, everyone would get one of these. This would not be soon enough for Nurse Slaney who might be one of the last to get one as she had just gone onto night duty. She decided to take matters into her own hands. With the help of a friend, she removed the mattress from the bed in the room she had just vacated, carried it up two flights of stairs and placed it in her new room. They then took the other mattress and put it in her old room.

How this was discovered, no one ever knew but on going to her room that evening, she found the old mattress back in place. Nurse Slaney remarked that she had taken all that trouble for nothing after all. Home Sister did not say anything to her although she must have known what had happened. However, in time, all the old mattresses were replaced with new ones.

Every Sunday afternoon while the patients had visitors, time was spent in cleaning the ward cupboards and sterilizers. It was a good opportunity to make sure that stocks of lotions were not depleted and to order anything in short supply to be brought from the pharmacy the following morning. We also made dressings and placed them in a large drum, which was then sterilised in an autoclave. Some of the patients were happy to help with these tasks especially if they did not have afternoon visitors. They were given rolls of gauze to cut into size and then folded to be used as dressings after being sterilised. Rolls of cotton wool were placed on the hot top of a sterilizer; this doubled the size and made the wool soft and pliable so it could then be rolled into balls ready for sterilizing.

The ward instrument sterilizers were emptied and cleaned before being refilled with water ready to boil any instruments required for dressings. At that time, everything was sterilised, instruments by boiling and dressings by being autoclaved. To remove the instruments from the sterilizer, long forceps known as Cheatles were used.

Each patient had an individual thermometer which was situated on the wall at the head of their bed. One afternoon, Norah collected all these and put them into a receiver, ready to wash and replace them in a clean sterile solution. Just as she entered the treatment room, she was called away and put the receiver containing the thermometers on to the first available clear surface which happened to be the sterilizer.

When she got back, it was to find that someone had switched on the sterilizer and the thermometers had all overheated and burst. At that time, anyone who broke a thermometer was expected to pay for it but to pay for thirty would have taken more than a month's salary. Norah had to go to Matron who was most understanding, perhaps realising that whoever had switched on the sterilizer was just as much to blame. Norah did not have to pay for any of the thermometers.

Many things were in short supply and we were expected to take good care of equipment. Syringes were made of glass and one had to be careful when sterilising these by placing them in cold water before boiling, so they did not break. Needles were precious and were taken away to be sharpened by the Medical Curator who also repaired other equipment when necessary. Nowadays, syringes and needles are ready sterilised for use in a sterile package but, sometimes blunt needles are found in these, I even found one without a point. It would have been extremely painful for the patient receiving medication with this so I found that it was important to check all needles before use.

There were many rules which were expected to be obeyed, some learned by experience, others by listening to our seniors. Some we did not know until we had broken them, an important rule was never to be late on duty without a good excuse. Any nurse who was persistently late on duty would be sent to Matron's office. Sometimes it was necessary to leave the dining room early to reach a ward as this often meant a long walk.

Nurses should never run even if someone was bleeding profusely, but were allowed to walk very quickly. This was probably a good rule for if the floor had recently been cleaned and was slippery, an accident might result.

As student nurses, we were not allowed to marry without Matron's consent, which meant that if someone wanted to marry, she had to leave and give up her training, even if she only had a few months before her finals.

However, one nurse *did* get married and managed to keep it secret until after her exam results came through. This is what happened.

Nurse Walsh was home on holiday having breakfast with her mother when her fiancé dashed in.

"We've got to get married," he said.

"It's usually the woman who says that," said her mother.

He was in a state of excitement as he sat down and told them his story.

Apparently, he was working for the Coal Board and had been allocated a house but could only accept this if he was married. After the war, there was an acute housing shortage and this chance was too good to miss. They could not possibly wait even three months until after she had taken her finals for by then someone else would have been given the house and she and her fiancé might have to wait months or even years before another became available. They obtained a special licence and were married. Nurse hid her wedding ring and came back to hospital to complete her training.

On the day of the examination results, she applied for Registration, gave in her notice and on her last day, put on her wedding ring. We all wished her well.

Soon back on days, Christmas was drawing close and once again, anyone who could was asked to help with a concert. This time it was a series of sketches and I wrote a poem that satirized several of the doctors and nurses who actually took it all in good part although today some of it would have been called racist. Part of the concert included the song,

'Dem Bones, dem dry Bones, hear the word of the Tute.'

For this, I enlisted the help of one of my friends and borrowed the skeleton from the Nurse Training School. We carefully wrapped 'Jimmy' in a sheet to carry him through the grounds and across the road to the concert hall.

All went well until we reached the pavement where the evening visitors were arriving. As we stood waiting to cross the road, a gust of wind blew the sheet off 'Jimmy's' head exposing his skull to the horror of some of the passing visitors. We quickly covered him and carried him across to the concert hall.

That year, Ward B 2 decided to decorate their ward to celebrate the ascent of Everest and managed to borrow many artifacts depicting the equipment used and pictures of the climber's progress. For this, they were awarded a prize by one of the Nursing Periodicals.

A few months before this, I had become friendly with Pat, one of the pupil mid-wives who had the room opposite mine in the Woodlands. We were both surprised to learn her home was not far from mine and her father was our GP.

One evening, Pat was late off duty and came to my room to explain why this had happened.

"I'm not going to stay long," she said.

"Have you had a busy day?"

"Oh yes; the worst, and to make things even more awful, I've just admitted a woman with head lice." She shuddered and scratched her head. "I'm sure I've caught them off her." She scratched her head again. "I'm going to wash my hair."

It was not uncommon to admit patients with head lice and fleas and as I later found out, some of the conditions they lived in did not help. Pat was tired but she stayed to talk to me until I too began to scratch my head. Even thinking about head lice was enough to make anyone imagine they were crawling through one's hair. At last Pat went away to get rid of the lice which I'm sure were imaginary and I gave my own hair a thorough brushing.

At that time midwifery training was taken in two parts and Pat had almost completed part one. As Selly Oak did not train midwives for the Part Two Module, she had arranged to do this in Derby.

When Pat finished her course, her colleagues decided to have a party and give her a good send off. That evening there was a lot of commotion on the second floor of the Nurses' Home as all her friends and a few gatecrashers gathered to wish her well. Luckily, Sister Carson the Home Sister was not on duty so there was no one to put an end to the high spirits. Even so, things started to get unruly and Pat tried to stop anyone else entering her room by locking the door. However, it was a shock to find two nurses she had evicted had returned. They had come in through the window as they had noticed a small balcony that ran between Pat's room and the one next door. The surprised occupant thought they were plunging to their death on the paving stones below and was relieved to find out that all was well.

Before Pat could announce that the fun was over, her friends wrapped her in a sheet and bundled her into a large linen basket which had been left at the top of the stairs. After this, they dragged it down the stairs, out through the main door, across the lawn and then across the cricket pitch which was between the two Nurses' Homes. Somehow, she escaped and ran back, arriving breathless in her room and everything went quiet as we all settled down for the night.

A few months later, I had a day out with a Health Visitor and found this quite interesting. We visited several mothers and babies and an elderly woman. In the afternoon, I helped at a baby clinic, a change to see healthy infants. This was a different aspect of nursing and one of which I would like to know more.

Many of our patients worked at the Cadbury chocolate factory in Bourneville or at the car factory further along the Bristol Road at

Longbridge. The factory at Bourneville had a flourishing Opera Group giving occasional performances to the local people. One evening, another student, Lisa, invited me to go with her to 'Carmen' and while enjoying the music we found that the part of Carmen was played by a lady whose size dwarfed the male singers. Despite the fact that she had a very good voice, we thought that this rather spoiled the show.

Although we could not afford to go out very often, on occasions, some of the Theatres in Birmingham sent spare tickets to the Hospital so that anyone who was off duty could take advantage of these. A notice was posted outside the Assistant Matrons' Office and news soon spread. In this way, I was able to see the D'Oyly Carte Opera Company in Ida and Yeomen of the Guard. On one occasion, I saw a musical and another time Pat and I were able to get tickets to hear a recital by a famous pianist who, I think, came from a European country. His name is forgotten but I remember that he brought his own piano with him which was pictured on the programme.

It was only rarely that we were given one of the better seats but I remember how enjoyable it was to have the opportunity to spend a night out which probably would never have happened if I had stayed at home.

THE THIRD YEAR

MORE LECTURES

During the following year we went into Nursing School for our third year lectures; this was harder than our previous study days. It did not help that the lecturers did not appear to be as good as those in our second year. Materia Medica, the study of drugs, was one of the subjects and should have been fascinating but the lecturer made it seem very dull. Luckily, there were books in the Nursing Library we could borrow to supplement our knowledge. How we wished that Dr Norton who had made everything so interesting and easy to learn in our second year could have given these lectures. At the end of this session, we had our final hospital exam and those of us who passed were rewarded with a third stripe.

At this time, I had been troubled with an impacted wisdom tooth and when the study days finished, I saw the dentist who arranged to remove this tooth on my day off. Unfortunately, it proved to be more difficult than expected and by the time he had finished my face and mouth, complete with several stitches, was quite swollen.

Later, that day, I went to the kitchen to make a hot drink as my mouth was too sore to eat anything. As I heated some milk, Sister Carson the Home Sister walked in and when she saw me told me to go to bed and she would bring me a drink. When she arrived she had some Paracetemol to give me and I realised that despite her stern exterior, like most of the other senior sisters, she was really kind and thoughtful.

In the morning, having slept well, I felt fine despite my swollen face, reporting on duty as usual. As it happened, I had to go to Sickbay that morning for a routine medical check. When Dr. Masterman saw me she took one look at me and said,

"I can't have you walking around the wards like that," and promptly sent me to bed in sickbay.

She then sent for the dentist who came and examined my stitches and put me on antibiotics. I spent three days there before being allowed back on duty. A few days later my stitches were removed and everything was satisfactory.

One thing we all worried about was being ill, for if we were off too long we had to make up any sick time and this might mean having to wait another three months before being allowed to take our finals. Luckily, the mishap with my tooth was not enough to prevent me taking my exams the following February.

While we were students, if anyone looked as if about to succumb to a cold by sneezing or coughing, we were sent straight to Sickbay where Sister there would administer her famous concoction, the mixture of Ammonia and Ether which made our symptoms disappear in a flash. Perhaps it was because of this, very few nurses became sick and had their Exams put back because of illness.

As the year progressed, we knew our State Exams were getting nearer and that we must study as much as possible. During this time, I worked on several different wards and this helped to consolidate the knowledge given in lectures.

As the year came to a close and Christmas loomed, I found myself on Ward C 3, Women's Medical, with Sister Carey, a staunch Roman Catholic.

In this, my final year, a new vicar came to Bourneville who was also the Hospital Chaplain. Once weekly, he came to the wards to see the patients and sing hymns. To encourage the patients to join in, he brought with him the small harmonium that belonged to the hospital and insisted on playing this as loud as he could despite sister asking him not to.

I remember one of our regular patients was Gwen, a diabetic woman who somehow managed to come in frequently to have her dose of Insulin stabilised. She was a likeable woman who managed to keep the patients entertained with stories about her exploits. She lived alone and I think she was lonely so her visits to hospital were a change for her. This particular afternoon, Gwen had to have some special tests that meant giving her an anaesthetic. She arrived back on the ward to the sound of the harmonium and as she was helped into bed, she asked, "Am I in heaven?" in a very loud voice.

As we removed the screens from around her bed, she sat up and pointed to the vicar and said, "I thought the music meant I was in heaven but seeing him and his little 'orgin' I know I'm not."

When the hymn ended the vicar left the ward rather quickly.

A rare condition was due to absence of thyroid hormone and was called cretinism. We saw one case of this when taken to visit a hospital for mentally subnormal people. This condition is rarely seen now as it is diagnosed in early life and can be treated successfully.

Many of our patients had chest infections that were brought on by the kind of work they did. In addition, at that time, the Clean Air Act was still in the future and during the winter months, the fogs were treacherous due to the smoke emitted by the furnaces that were needed by some of the factories in the town. Sometimes this was so thick outside, it even permeated through the wards. The smoke and fog mingled together and became known as 'smog'.

This Christmas I found myself in demand to help decorate the ward and had the idea of painting sprigs of holly or mistletoe on the round lights above each bed. Watercolours were chosen because the paint would wash off easily when Christmas ended.

I became more ambitious and painted angels on some of the lights that pleased Sister who then demanded that I paint the Madonna and child on the central larger lights. This took much longer and as I could only work at this during off duty time, it left me with little time to myself. Viewed from a distance when the lights were on, the paintings looked quite pleasing. A closer look would show the imperfections in my painting but everyone seemed happy with the result.

The patients were disappointed when two days after Christmas the Deputy Matron insisted that these were removed even though they were not thought to be a fire hazard as most of the other decorations. As I painted the lamps, I could not help wondering where I would be when next Christmas came. There was no time to speculate on the future for the Final Examinations loomed and every spare minute had to be spent in revision.

This year, the hospital Chaplain decided to help with the Christmas Eve Carols and brought the Church Choir and some of the congregation with him. The nurses brought up the rear of the procession and as we left one ward, we could hear the singers who were just entering the next block. To my amazement, they were singing another hymn whilst we had hardly finished the previous one. Later, I wrote a poem about this which is reproduced here –

CHRISTMASES REMEMBERED

I remember Christmas.

Off-duty voluntarily suspended.
The time used to decorate wards. At night
when daylight ended, tints softly blended.
Water-coloured angels on each side light.
Simple Madonna and Child were centred
on main ward lights. Shimmering like stained glass,
capturing the eyes of all who entered
the ward, to give the message of Christmas.

Christmas Eve carols, cloaks scarlet outside,
Improvised lanterns carried, all lights dim.
Day's duties ended, ward doors opened wide.
Ethereal voices singing, made each hymn
unforgettable. Patients, friends and all
were silent as we passed. Our aching feet
forgotten, and tomorrow's early call
still distant. The Eve of Christmas, complete.

And in my final year, a new Chaplain,
thought it his duty to join our song.
He came, bringing choir and congregation.
Nurses behind, the crocodile so long,
all the choirboys at the front were singing
a new carol, while at the rear, outcast,
walking slowly, lanterns gently swinging,
the nurses sang the ending of the last.

Another Christmas, in another year.
A family just returned from the east,
no father, no home, nothing to bring cheer,
the children bewildered, their fear increased.
Then people came, to help and show they cared
carrying gifts of food toys and a tree
adorned with decorations, lights which flared
gaily cheering the room for all to see.

Yes, I remember Christmas.

The last verse was of an incident I shall never forget. It happened many years later when I became a Health Visitor working in a Northern Town.

FINAL EXAMINATIONS

Soon after Christmas, it was a surprise to be moved to Ward L on Night Duty. Expecting to stay on Ward C 3 until after taking State Finals this came as a shock. Naturally, this was disappointing at this particular time as I said to Sister Partington, our Tutor.

"Night duty is so tiring, I won't be able to study as much as I would like."

"You've done well so far," she reminded me, "and you will get nights off for the Revision days and also before taking your Finals."

With this, I had to be content.

Ward L was Babies and Toddlers Medical and although spending some time on Ward F, Children's Medical, the work on L was quite different. The nurse on duty with me was Anne who was a trained Sick Children's Nurse and was now working for her General Certificate. On this ward, her specialist knowledge of children proved to be very helpful.

After arriving on the ward and directly after being given the report, there were twelve ill babies to feed. This took most of our time and we were glad that the toddlers, who slept most of the night, only required supervision and regular medication whilst we were there.

One disadvantage was that this ward was divided into four separate rooms, two downstairs and two upstairs, the ward office being upstairs. Although there were only six cots in each, it meant that we were constantly going up and down a stone staircase to make sure all was well. There were also open fires in the upstairs wards that needed to be kept burning otherwise the ward temperature became too low. Because of these fires, somewhere in one of the wards a cricket chirped constantly throughout the night.

The walls in all the wards were tiled and had a frieze depicting some of the Beatrix Potter animals such as Peter Rabbit.

One lesson quickly learned was that trying to hurry a baby's feed could be disastrous for as soon as the last drop was swallowed the baby would be sick. Therefore, however much work there was to do, it was best to sit quietly as if there was all the time in the world and talk quietly to the infant. In this way, the nurse and baby were relaxed and the feed stayed down. This experience proved useful during my midwifery training.

Soon after arrival on the ward, often the phone would ring,

"This is Sister Thompson; I'm sending a nurse to help with the baby feeds."

This could be a mixed blessing for it took a while for a new nurse to get into the routine. Most soon adapted but some nights she sent a male nurse who somehow was not able to manage to feed any baby without it being sick as soon as the feed was finished. We tried to give him those babies to feed who were on the way to recovery but he still found difficulty in feeding young babies. Where possible we gave him other jobs to do and got on with feeding and changing the babies ourselves.

One night he arrived and said to me, "I'm sure Night Sister said to me, 'Nurse go to Hell'."

At this thought, I smiled but did not comment, thinking perhaps that was what she had really meant. Previously, when on Male Surgical night duty, he had been my junior and when things were busy, he always seemed to disappear.

The week of my Finals came and even though given time off to revise, I felt totally unprepared. On examination day, I looked at the paper in front of me and froze. In that terrible moment, my mind became completely blank and everything went out of my head. The minutes ticked by but I could not think of a single answer but just sat there becoming more panic stricken as the hands of the clock moved forward. Everyone around was writing industriously whilst I sat in a daze unable to lift my pen.

Then at last, it seemed as if the haze clouding my mind lifted and reading the questions once more, I gave myself a mental shake. This time, there was at least one question that seemed easier than the others. Having written everything I could remember on that subject, I went on to answer the next question and could hardly believe, when told to put our pens down, that I had answered the correct number of questions. After this, I found the remaining papers, though not easy, did not send me into such confusion again.

The practical exam was the following week and this was held at another hospital where two examiners asked us questions in turn. They also gave us practical tasks such as setting up trays and trolleys for different procedures. At last, it was over and the weeks of waiting began. In many ways, it was better to be on a busy ward for there was less time to think and worry about the outcome.

In the weeks that followed, the ward seemed busier than ever; a six-month-old baby with toxoplasmosis had been with us since he was three months old. We had watched his development and were glad when little Colin was able to go home. Although we missed him, we were glad that at last his parents would share the joy of watching him grow. But there was no time to wonder how he progressed for there were many other emergencies such as a small child with croup necessitating a steam tent and more worried parents to reassure,

Another baby who was Rhesus negative needed a 'top up' blood transfusion. This kept us busy with no time to feel tired until off duty in the morning. The blood needed careful monitoring for little Peter must only receive a certain amount. This had been marked on the bottle for blood came only in fixed quantities. This was watched very carefully so that as soon as the required quantity had been given, the drip could be removed. Anne went to her meal just as Night Sister arrived and we walked through the wards together, stopping at Peter's cot and noting that he had almost received the required amount of blood.

As soon as sister left, I went back to check the blood, looking up at the bottle and with shock, found the bottle empty. How could this have happened? Surely the blood had not run through in such a short time. As the thought went through my mind, I looked at the floor and saw a large pool of blood which was what was left of the contents of the bottle. Then I noticed that the drip connection was undone and realised the baby must have woken and kicked this. Perhaps Sister and I had disturbed him when we went to look at his drip.

I rang Sister to tell her what had happened,

"It's about little Peter, Sister. His drip connection must have been loose and came undone, the bottle is empty and the blood has drained to the floor."

"Well, he had nearly had enough when I saw him ten minutes ago. Take the drip down and we'll let the doctors decide about it in the morning."

"It was almost down to the mark, Sister."

"Just keep an eye on him the rest of the night."

"Yes Sister. Thank you."

Peter looked a good colour and slept through any disturbance made as a dressing was placed on his arm where the needle had been. After this, the floor was cleaned as only a little blood could make a very large mess.

One night an extremely ill child was rushed in just after midnight and though the doctors did everything they could to help her, she died soon after admission. Laying out a dead person is sad at any time but when it is a child, more so and both Anne and I had to fight back our tears that morning. Anne found a few white flowers to place in the child's hands before asking the porters to take her away.

Another night, a very ill child who needed an oxygen tent and constant attention was admitted. His parents stayed with him all night and did not move from Timothy's side. I did everything I could to help him and when the day staff arrived there seemed some improvement in his condition. I went off duty, my mind on this sick child hoping he would get well.

Arriving at the dining room I found everyone milling around outside the Assistant Matrons' office in an excited mood.

"How did you get on?" someone asked and I stared at her not realizing what she meant. I'd completely forgotten the Final Results were due that morning.

Someone pushed me towards the office where I found Sister Partington with a sheaf of envelopes in her hand. As she handed one to me she smiled.

"Come on, open it," someone behind me said and with shaking hands I tore it open. I could hardly believe it but all the studying had resulted in a pass. My tiredness left me as in a state of sudden exhilaration, I went into the dining room although too excited to eat.

The first thing after this was to telephone a neighbour of my parents and ask her to let my mother and father know about my success. Later, my father was so pleased he told everyone he met in the village that his daughter had passed her exams and was now a qualified nurse.

After filling in the necessary forms, the next thing was go to the post office in Selly Oak. Attempting to draw out enough money from my small savings account to apply for Registration with the General Nursing Council, there was a problem. The assistant thought that the signature in my Post Office Savings Book was not the same as the one on the Withdrawal Form. In addition, the original Post Office was many miles away.

"But I'm working at Selly Oak Hospital where I've been training to become a nurse for the last three years. I was only fifteen when I started saving." I told her, "my writing has obviously changed since then."

"I see," she said. "Have you any identification?"

"Only these," I said, showing my application forms containing my name.

In those days, there were no credit cards and few people drove cars so I was not likely to have a driving licence. In my excitement, I had forgotten about the identity card we had all been issued with during the war.

She looked at me appraisingly, then smiled, took the withdrawal form and passed most of my savings back to me so that I was able to buy a Postal Order to send for Registration.

By the time I returned to the Nurses' Home, I felt tired but found it hard to get to sleep in the excitement that at last I had achieved my goal.

One morning a few days later, Matron sent for me and offered me a post as Staff Nurse on Ward D.5 as soon as my Registration came through. I was happy to accept this, knowing that since working previously on that ward, a different sister was in charge.

Soon my time on night duty came to an end and as I had holiday due together with nights off, I had some time at home. Reminding my brother Gordon of the promise he had made at the end of my first three months, he kept his word and bought me a silver belt buckle which I was eventually able to wear.

STAFF NURSE

Arriving back at the hospital, a new uniform was waiting; this was pale blue with a matching blue belt. The apron had a bib instead of straps and putting it on, I felt as if with it I also assumed knowledge and authority. At the same time, the realisation that there was still much to learn and this was just the beginning.

On the ward, I was one of two staff nurses, the other; Staff Nurse Astin was now part time, as she had recently married. At that time, very few married women were employed as nurses so an exception had been made for her. Although her parents' home was only a short distance from the Woodlands, she was not allowed to live at home during training. On passing her finals, she was able to live at home where she prepared for her marriage. After this, she was given a post on Ward A 5. Although only a few months senior to me, Joy was already used to staff nurse duties and helped me to settle into my new ward duties.

This not only consisted of acting as Sister's deputy when both she and Nurse Astin were off duty, also ward rounds with the doctors and consultants and teaching the student nurses.

During this time, my knowledge of each patient increased from listening and taking notice of what the doctors said on the ward rounds. As I got to know individual patients and observe them, I was often able to notice changes that sometimes could be almost imperceptible. Most of my time on duty was spent with the patients;

assisting in training student nurses helped me to consolidate the knowledge gained during my own training.

The consultant on this ward was Doctor Norton who had given lectures on Medicine in my second year and I learned even more from him on ward rounds.

Another consultant had only a few beds on the ward and on one occasion came to visit his patients when I was in charge. His houseman hurried to open the ward door for him with the intention of following him and leaving me at the rear. Dr Woods turned and said, "After you, Staff Nurse," standing back for me to lead the way. This was typical of his approach to both staff and patients but not all the doctors and surgeons were like this.

Each ward took it in turns to be on call for emergencies and Monday was usually one of our days. One of our most frequent admissions on that day were women who had taken an overdose of drugs, usually aspirin after a weekend that had probably been rather fraught. This necessitated them having a stomach wash out to remove as much of the drug they had taken as possible but was not a pleasant procedure for the patient. Perhaps it acted as a deterrent so that they did not try to do it a second time. At that time, taking one's own life was a criminal act and involved an interview with the police. Judging by the women I treated; it seemed much more likely to be a cry for help. As it was usually my task to administer treatment, I learned a lot about the reasons for this action. Many of these women had large families as at this time; the contraceptive pill was unheard of. After a busy weekend looking after their large families without help, they were often tired and very unhappy about their circumstances. It was a sobering thought to know that marriages did not always have a happy ending.

One of our regular patients, a woman of thirty-five with Down's syndrome who also had diabetes needed her urine tested regularly.

Each time I did this, she asked, "Is my water any better, nurse?" On reassurance, she would give me a hug. She was affectionate and hugged everyone who was kind to her. I have since heard that people with Downs could be very aggressive but as a nurse, I never found this to be so. Dawn's parents were nearing retirement age and I often wondered how they would cope with caring for her as they grew older.

One Friday afternoon, I had just arrived in my room in the Nurses Home when I was called to the telephone. I hurried downstairs wondering who it could be and found it was my older brother, Gordon.

"Can you come home?" he asked.

"Why, what's the trouble?" I replied.

"It's David, he's not well and you know mum and dad are away in Jersey until tomorrow night."

"What exactly is the matter?"

"He's got very bad stomach pains and he's been sick. I've called the doctor."

"I'll see if I can get time off and let you know."

He gave me his telephone number and I hurried back to the Assistant Matron's office. The Sister there heard my story and reluctantly said I could go but I must let them know what was happening as soon as possible. If I was away for long, someone would have to take my place on the ward.

I arrived home later to find my younger brother David looking flushed but was sleeping. The doctor had been and would call again in the morning.

I rang the hospital and told the Assistant Matron on duty that it seemed that it was his appendix but at the moment, he seemed fairly comfortable.

"Stay as long as you need but keep in touch," was the reply.

After a fairly good night, by morning, David was complaining of pain which had now localised. I rang the GP who said he would visit before surgery.

Before long, David was in the local Hospital undergoing an operation to remove his appendix. All was well when I rang the ward so I then contacted Selly Oak to let them know I would be back the following morning. Later, Gordon came over to meet mother and father off the bus that evening.

Naturally, my mother was upset about things, "Why didn't you let us know?" she said.

"You couldn't have got here any sooner," Gordon said.

Having placated my mother, I was glad, I had been able to tidy the house before she arrived as David had left his weeks washing up and several other things, intending to sort things out on the Saturday.

Arriving back at Selly Oak about half past eleven, I reported to the office. Sister Parker said very little to me but as I was leaving the office, Sister James called me back,

"How is your brother, Nurse?" she asked.

Back on the ward, I found that things had been quiet as luckily we had not been on call that weekend.

One day, Matron sent for me and approaching her office, I wondered what had necessitated this summons. She had decided I was suitable to enter a Speech Making Competition to take place at the Queen Elizabeth Hospital. Why she had chosen me out of all the other nurses, I do not know but perhaps it had something to do with my activities in the Christmas Concerts. It took several days of wondering what to talk about before an idea for a subject occurred.

The hall was full of other students, most of them taking part but being apprehensive about my own part in the procedure, the topics others had discussed were completely forgotten afterwards. One thing I remember was how confident many of them seemed and when my speech was over I was glad to return to my seat. It may have been defeatist but after watching the others, I realised my chances of success were slight.

In July, the Nurses Reunion was held; this was also the occasion for the Prize giving and certificates to those who had completed their training. It seemed that perhaps I had not done too badly at Speech making for Matron asked me to give the vote of thanks to the important people who attended. I received the Third Year Nursing Prize and was pleased that my friend Norah received Matron's Prize for 'The Nurse Who Had Made The Most Effort.'

One afternoon I was off duty and had just arrived in the Nurses Home when someone came to tell me I had a visitor. Thinking this might be my aunt or cousin, I hurried downstairs to the hall. A man who was a complete stranger stood there and I wondered what he wanted. It was quite a shock to find that he thought I wanted to buy a complete set of the Encyclopaedia Britannica which at that time cost over one hundred pounds, about half my yearly salary. He was adamant that I had sent an application to have someone call to take my order.

"On my pay," I said, "it would take several years to pay for them."

With that, he went away and left me wondering who had sent this request but it was something I never found out.

Something learned whilst working on A 5 was how easy it could be for a patient to conceal their medication. Mrs Carson had been given her medication regularly with a drink of water and it did seem that she had swallowed the tablets.

Mrs Carson was actually the mother of one of the Sisters who one day, when tidying her locker found a large number of tablets. Mrs. Carson made it appear as if she was swallowing the tablets but had concealed them in her cheek or under her tongue and then spit them out. After this incident, we were careful to make sure any medication given to her was swallowed. I do not think she intended to save them, in order to take them all at once but we had to make sure it would not happen.

On another occasion, an elderly woman was admitted to a side ward with a circulatory problem. Sadly, this resulted in amputation of one leg but Agnes, as she insisted we call her, did not feel sorry for herself but took delight in teasing the nurses. One day, the doctors, consultant, registrar and houseman arrived at her bed during a ward round.

Agnes took one look at them and said, "Well, I am honoured, three doctors, at least *they* are doctors," she pointed to the consultant and registrar and then looked at the houseman, "and *he* thinks he is."

Everyone laughed except the houseman who looked rather embarrassed.

Another time, I was behind the screen with Agnes when someone came into the ward.

"Are you there, Penny?" a voice asked.

"Penny? Who is that?" asked Agnes.

"It's me," I said.

"Penny? You! You're not worth that much, I shall call you Nurse Farthing," she said.

Having grown fond of Agnes, it was impossible to object.

Time went by quickly on the ward and although I enjoyed the work, I began to feel that it was time to move on. Many senior staff reminded me that I would not be properly trained until I became a midwife. For this, I could stay at Selly Oak and move to Ward D. 5 or apply to another hospital and this is what I did.

Derby City Hospital was the training school that was my choice to do Part One midwifery and possibly, to follow my friend Pat to the Queen Mary Nursing Home to complete Part Two. It was not long before I learned that I had been allocated a place to start on the first of November that year.

When the day finally came for me to leave Selly Oak, I was sorry for I had made many friends there. Although knowing little about midwifery training I felt less apprehensive about starting something new. I had arrived just over three and a half years before with one suitcase; I left with two suitcases and a number of packages that gave me some difficulty on the journey. Luckily, my brother, Gordon collected me from the railway station and took me home.

MOVING ON

MIDWIFERY

Situated on the outskirts of Derby, The City Hospital was not too far from my home which made it easier to visit my family. I was soon to find the work and studying very hard, for there was an enormous amount to learn in the six months allocated for the first part of the Midwifery Certificate.

Our tutor, whom we all grew to like, was called Miss Gorman who gave us all an enthusiasm to become midwives. Whilst making sure that we always worked hard at our studies, she had a sense of humour and kept quiet about many of our escapades. The Labour Ward was run very efficiently by Sister Rendel who, with others taught most of the practical side of our work.

Now we were no longer either students or staff nurses but demoted, or so it seemed to the bottom of the hierarchy as pupil midwives, The other pupil midwives consisted of three other State Registered Nurses who like myself were new and several who were taking an eighteen month course for Registration in Part One. We would all do six months for Part Two of the Midwifery Certificate then after passing the final examination; we would become State Certified Midwives. .Among the other students were two Nigerians, Gracie from Ghana, several English and one French pupil, Madeleine, who kept us all amused, especially when telling us about the uniform she had found waiting for her when she first arrived.

"Eet was impossible," she exclaimed throwing her arms out to demonstrate.

"Why?" we asked.

"Eet was enormous. Eet was big as a tent."

We all looked sympathetic as we asked. "Why?"

"Those women in the sewing room. They inseest they make the right measurement. The measure I sent."

"What went wrong?" we were eager to learn more.

"They inseest I send wrong measurement. But, I say, this is like a tent. They said it could not possibly happen and found my letter." She paused, we waited.

"I am French and in France it is the centimetre we use which is smaller than your inch so they make eighty eight inches instead of eighty eight centimetres. I am not so fat, I tell them and at last they understand but they are very cross."

The remaining two pupils were both English, and had already completed three months of the course. One of these was diabetic but this did not deter her from the hard work entailed. The other lived on the Duffield Road in Derby but as previously, everyone had to live in hospital accommodation.

In Derby, we did not have a Home Sister but a Warden, a rather grim woman who treated us as if we could not be trusted. Her attitude tended to bring out our worst behaviour though we tried not to be caught in our misdemeanours.

The food was not nearly as good as it had been at Selly Oak with little extra available on the ante and post - natal wards. After delivery, mothers were often hungry or unable to sleep but they could not even have a slice of toast although occasionally we were able to make them a cup of tea.

Madeleine had a great deal to say about the food; being French she knew a lot about the way food is prepared in her own country. She often threw up her hands in horror at some of the concoctions served up in the dining room.

"Thees ees not food for 'ungry workers," she exclaimed and upset one of the dining room maids by telling them to empty it into the bin.

In our sitting room, a notice board held what was known as the 'Change List'; this had to be checked frequently so that we knew to which ward we were being moved as this could happen suddenly.

Before we were allowed to have anything to do with the women in labour, we had to attend and witness ten births; this was twenty for the eighteen-month pupils. After this, we were allowed to deliver our first baby under the supervision of a trained midwife.

I shall never forget the first birth I saw for when the baby was born he looked a very deep shade of blue and for a moment, I thought he was not alive. Then he took a breath and yelled loudly and in moments, his colour changed to pink. At this stage and for a long time after, his fingers and toes still looked blue but the midwife told us this was natural and would gradually improve.

Wherever we were, on the labour ward or on one of the postnatal wards, if the phone rang to say a birth was imminent, we had to rush down to the labour ward and watch the birth. Often, if we were doing something that could not be left, we arrived too late. Despite this, very soon we had witnessed ten births but the eighteen-month students having to witness twice as many took much longer. After this, we were sent in turn to work on the labour ward to learn about labour and what to watch for.

Lectures began almost immediately and our tutor was good at explaining about the different stages of normal labour. It helped to be able to relate what we saw in the labour ward with what we were taught. As we progressed, she taught us about abnormal labour and how to deal with problems in pregnancy. A very important point she drilled into us was patience.

"Always be patient, it's when you become impatient and try to rush things that something goes wrong," she told us.

Another time she said, "Never let the patient see that you are worried because the moment she starts to think something is wrong, she will tense all her muscles and then there *will* be problems."

We soon found that her words were true and that this knowledge could only come from years of practice as a midwife. Later, in trying to follow her teaching to not let patients know if their condition was worrying, has helped them and me.

With the help of our tutor and the Midwifery sisters on the wards, a good grounding was given to us in the conduct of pregnancy and labour. The approach was essentially 'hands on' with the importance of reassuring the patient and keeping her informed about her own progress.

"Always tell the patient what you are about to do," was emphasised by the tutor throughout.

The general work on the wards was not difficult and Sister Rendel and her deputy who were very experienced midwives made work on the labour wards interesting. Midwifery, they emphasised, involves complete cooperation between nurse and patient. We found we could consolidate our practical knowledge on the wards by looking up the relevant actions we had seen in the textbook written by Margaret Myles[1]. Whatever we were taught could be found in this book and it became the one aid we felt we could not manage without during our training and later. It was studied and consulted all the time and became a necessary part of our lives for it seemed that everything we needed to know was covered by her.

When a new patient was admitted, she was examined, first to find out how far on she was in her pregnancy, a procedure known as palpating. After first warming, one's hands were then placed on the

---

1 A Textbook For Midwives. Margaret F. Myles. First Edition, 1953. (Reprinted 1955)

abdomen and the height of the uterine fundus ascertained by which means one knew where to listen to the foetal heart. This was done by means of a Pinard's stethoscope, a small trumpet shaped instrument that is placed on the abdomen and the midwife's ear placed at the other end. An experienced midwife will know in which position the baby is lying when she has palpated the abdomen, and be able to place the stethoscope in the correct position. After this, the blood pressure is taken and if all is well, the mother is prepared for her delivery.

In addition to delivering the baby and making both mother and baby comfortable after taking them to one of the lying-in wards, we had to strip and disinfect the bed, sluice any blood off the sheets and mop the floor, wash the bed with disinfectant and make it ready for the next patient. Although there were four labour wards, this had to be accomplished quickly as there always seemed to be another mother waiting for a bed.

One day, I had just finished and was putting my equipment away feeling very hot and flustered for I had to prepare another room, when Margaret walked into the labour ward.

"You look as if you're having a hot flush," she remarked with a grin.

I thought nothing of this until going off duty and found she had written on a large Cow and Gate poster,

'Penny complains of hot flushes, is she on the 'Change' List?'

By the time we had finished the course, this poster was completely covered with the amusing remarks written there.

Although after a few weeks we were allowed to deliver babies on our own, a trained midwife always had to be present. We were encouraged to do everything just as we had been taught and the midwife let us get on without interfering unless this was absolutely necessary. In this way, we received a good grounding in the practical side of midwifery.

Work on the lying-in wards was also important, for those of the mothers with stitches were often uncomfortable. At that time, they had to stay in bed for several days and regular routine swabbing of the genital area had to be carried out to prevent infection. Babies had to be helped to breast feed which was not always easy even when the infant was hungry. If the mother was not comfortable because of her stitches, the infant seemed to sense this and struggled instead of fixing on the breast. The mothers found this quite distressing and were often in tears. Having made the mother more comfortable, the baby would settle down and feed quite well. This was better for the mother because if the baby would not 'fix' properly, the nipples became quite sore and caused even more problems.

After a normal delivery, mothers were kept in hospital for ten days or longer if their baby had been delivered by Caesarean Section. Most mothers did not object to this, as they were glad of a rest away from their demanding families; usually they had a close relative who would help out at home. If not, sometimes the mother would agitate to get home so that her husband could return to work. Quite often, a mother would become worried about this and discharge herself against medical advice so that she could be at home with the children.

Unlike Selly Oak, we were only issued with two ward dresses which meant that when our soiled dresses were sent to the laundry, we only had one dress to wear and if this became grubby, we did not have a fresh one until the clean laundry came back. This could be difficult as the clean laundry came back on the same day the soiled items were sent. Occasionally, although not too often, as we wore long white gowns over our uniform most of the time, it meant washing the ward dresses ourselves.

One week, having arranged for Margaret to collect my clean laundry and send off my soiled dress and aprons before I left on nights off, I came back to find to my horror, that no dress had been returned.

Could this be an unkind joke? Had someone taken it or was it a mistake and my dress placed in the wrong package? I went to Margaret's room and told her of my dilemma. She had no idea where my dress might be as she had taken the unopened package and put it in my room.

So what could I do? Anyone who might be able to loan me a dress in a suitable size was on duty that night which left me with a big problem.

"You can borrow mine and go to the laundry in the morning to see what happened to yours," was Margaret's idea as she was off that night.

This was the only answer but as she was at least four inches taller and also broader than me, it created other problems. In the end, with a false hem stitched with black thread and a copious supply of safety pins, I was dressed and ready to go on duty. My apron concealed some of the limitations of the dress but that night I kept out of sight as much as possible and wore a gown most of the time. At meal times I did receive some odd looks from the student nurses. Luckily, that night I was on one of the lying-in wards, not the labour ward where my dress might have suffered complete disintegration. What a relief when in the morning I could go to the laundry and collect a clean dress in my own size.

During our training, an event took place which fascinated us all. This was the wedding of the film star, Grace Kelly and Prince Rainier of Monaco. We watched the television eagerly and teased each other over who would apply for the post of Royal Midwife if one was needed at some future date. This occasion was one we were all keen to see and talk about and made a change from our studies.

PROBLEMS

Whether on Day or Night Duty, when coming off duty, we were always ready for a refreshing bath but in the mornings, especially after a busy night on duty often, we were so tired we found ourselves falling asleep. Luckily, someone would bang on the door and waken us before we did so.

Sometimes our tiredness had the opposite effect and we would make rather too much noise for Miss Lewis, the warden. She would appear almost out of nowhere to tell us to be quiet, leaving with threats about informing the matron about us. This usually subdued us for about a week or until something else was found to be noisy about.

One evening, after a busy day on the labour ward, feeling sleepy, I was relaxing in the luxury of a hot bath when I heard running water in the next bathroom. I took no notice of this until I stepped out of my bath into a pool of warm water.

Slipping quickly into my dressing gown, I hurried next door and found the taps running and the bath overflowing in a cascade onto the floor. I turned off the taps, pulled out the plug and called for help. All the other pupil midwives who were not on duty, turned out together with anything that could be found to mop up the mess. We found the mop and bucket in the cleaner's cupboard and used this along with any cloths and towels. There seemed to be so much water but eventually it was clear. Luckily, these bathrooms were on the ground floor so there was no problem of water seeping through a ceiling.

All this time, we had been dreading to hear Miss Lewis's voice adding this to our list of crimes. It was amazing that she did not appear and we never found out who had left that bath running.

In midwifery, we learned about a flood of a different kind; this happened when an expectant mother's waters broke unexpectedly. The main problem when this occurred could be that if the baby's head was high, the cord might prolapse between the baby's head and the pelvis. Then as the head descended during labour, the cord could be compressed against the pelvis cutting off the blood supply to the infant. This is an emergency situation and quite often, the patient has to have an emergency Caesarean section. Luckily, this situation is rare but I soon found that in midwifery, no one panicked but did what was necessary quietly and promptly.

Delivering a baby is not always as easy as it may look and although the majority of babies are born without problems, there are many things that can go wrong. Part of our training made us aware of how to recognise difficulties and to know when to call for help. One of our training aids was a life-sized doll and a human pelvis through which we had to guide the doll in, through, and out under the pelvic arch in a series of moves known as mechanisms. We became quite skilled in this procedure and often could be heard chanting these mechanisms to ourselves. This helped us to anticipate how to assist at an actual birth.

Quite early in the course we were put onto night duty where we worked on the labour ward in turn. This meant we were soon able to get the number of deliveries required by the Central Midwives Board to pass our exams. The number required was ten but most of us were able to deliver many more than that, and with each baby safely born, become more proficient.

Lectures had to be attended in our own time and this often meant being late to bed for some were at eleven in the morning, finishing about midday. Others were at four in the afternoon, which meant getting up about half past three. On the occasions when we had lectures morning and evening, we were rather tired at night as we only had about four hours sleep. It was better to be on one of the lying-in wards which were quieter rather than the labour wards. The consultants gave these lectures but Miss Gorman, the tutor was more considerate and arranged her lectures at convenient times. We cheered each other up by indulging in high spirits when not too tired, making sure Miss Lewis, the Warden was not nearby.

One of our jokes was to 'award' any of the group with a 'gold medal' if a question was answered correctly in class. At first this was just telling the student she had won the distinction but one day, Margaret came back from her day off with a large medal she had made. This consisted of a round piece of gold cardboard with red ribbons sewn around it. Any pupil who had managed to give good answers in class found it hanging on her door, causing great amusement. Gracie in particular went into fits of laughter when she discovered it on her door one evening. The tutor, Miss Gorman thought this was very amusing but Miss Lewis the warden did not approve at all.

Although during night duty, our rooms were in a separate wing on the top floor Miss Lewis often heard us talking and we were blamed for waking the other night staff.

Most of us were qualified State Registered nurses but we found the student nurses from the General Wards seemed to ignore us and at meal times rarely spoke to us. Perhaps the prefix 'pupil' made us seem inferior but though we tried to be friendly, we were disregarded except by one male nurse who sometimes joined us at our table.

One night as three of us walked along the corridor to the dining room for our midnight meal, Annie saw an empty laundry trolley outside one of the General Wards. Always full of fun, she decided to go for a ride and sitting on this she said to Margaret and me, "Come on, give me a push."

Thinking it would only be for a short distance, we did so, not realising the corridor sloped downward towards the General Night Sister's Office. The trolley suddenly gained momentum and unable to stop it, we watched as it careered along. Further down, it came to rest against the wall outside the Office. Annie scrambled to her feet and looked up to be met by the steely gaze of the Night Sister. However, Annie did not let this bother her, as she said,

"Good evening Sister," and hurried back to join us.

One evening, before going on duty, Margaret and I went to the Queen Mary Nursing Home to see my friend Pat whom I had met at Selly Oak. We were surprised to see that the midwives lived in an ancient Victorian building which looked as if nothing had been done to renovate it since it was built. Even the plumbing was quite antiquated and we wondered what the hospital facilities were like. Pat told us the conditions were not very good. After this, we discussed what we had seen and decided not to take Part Two of our training there.

This meant we had to see Matron and tell of our decision. Naturally, she was not too pleased although we had not made a definite commitment to go on to do Part Two training in Derby. She said we must leave as soon as we had completed our six months Part One training. This was quite a blow for although we were due two weeks paid leave, we would have two weeks without income. This meant we would have to manage with the help of our parents, for to get work for just two weeks would be impossible.

Meantime we both wrote to various training schools and I was offered a place at Heathfield Maternity Hospital in Handsworth, Birmingham. Margaret found a Hospital near her own home and we promised to meet together and exchange experiences later.

The antenatal clinic at the City hospital was extremely busy but the Sister in charge gave the pupils plenty of opportunity to examine the patients. In those days, scans had not yet become available and the only means of checking how far the pregnancy had progressed was by palpating the abdomen and asking relevant questions. After working with Sister Jones we soon learned to be reasonably accurate at this. Most patients remembered when they first felt their baby move and this was helpful in estimating the delivery date.

To check the baby's heartbeat, we used the Pinard's stethoscope. If a doctor's stethoscope was available it was possible to let the mother listen too which was always a thrill for them.

One day, the clinic was busy and Sister called to me to take several mothers who were nearing their due dates to a quiet part of the waiting room and to show them the equipment used in labour.

"Tell them the 'Gas and Air' story," she said.

"What do you mean?" I asked.

"Well tell them about the ways discomfort in labour can be helped by the use of certain drugs and the Gas and Air machine."

Being unused to talking to several patients at once, I felt nervous but as the patients asked questions, I became more confident. Each patient was shown how to put the mask over her face and breathe in deeply. This was the only way, the mixture of gas and air would enter their lungs and give relief. The theory was that if they inhaled too much, the mixture would make them sleepy and relaxed and they would loosen their hold on the mask and breathe in normal air. I practice I often found that this was not true as most patients seemed to tighten their grip on the mask, making it difficult to remove.

I also had to tell them what would happen when they came into the labour ward and about other ways we could help make labour easier. Apart from my efforts at the Speech Making contest and the Vote of thanks whilst at Selly Oak this was a new experience but after several sessions in the clinic I soon became used to talking to a different group of patients.

Back on the Labour Ward, several of the mothers I had seen in clinic came into the ward in early labour. They were prepared for delivery and taken into the First Stage Room where there were six beds. One night, Sister gave one mother a barbiturate sedative to help her sleep. Everything seemed quiet but about an hour later, after delivering a baby and clearing up afterwards, I went to see if anyone needed anything and found this woman wandering around in a disoriented state. I managed to calm her and get her back into bed and told Sister what had happened. It appeared that occasionally barbiturate drugs could have this effect on women in labour. I watched her carefully for the rest of the night. Eventually her labour was established and she delivered a baby boy later the following morning.

Most of us were given the opportunity to be present in the delivery rooms, either to deliver normal births or to watch more complicated deliveries such as twin or breech births. Usually one of twins would be breech and to make sure that this baby was delivered slowly and carefully was more than our skills had yet mastered. Most babies are born in the conventional way, that is 'anterior occiput' with the back of the baby's head uppermost. Sometimes a baby was born with its face upward which could give problems but there was always a skilled midwife there to help the pupil through any difficulties.

In the classroom, we learned about the various positions a baby might be born in but most of these are rare and we did not see any at the City. On occasion, a mother might be admitted with high blood pressure, this sometimes developed into pre-eclampsia, a condition seen in some pregnancies. This could cause fits which could be dangerous to both mother and baby. This development had to be prevented by sedation and in many of these cases, the baby was born by Caesarean Section and after delivery; the mother's blood pressure usually began to fall and become more normal. Other types of delivery are fairly rare and we did not see any during our Part One Training.

The time came for our exam which was taken at Loveday Street Maternity Hospital in Birmingham before we finished our time in Derby. Afterwards we went into a Kardoma Café for coffee and cake to discuss our answers. This 'post mortem' is something I have always hated because it made me think about the answers I should have given and the wrong answers I'm sure I did give.

Luckily, it was not too long before our results were posted to us and despite our misgivings, we had all passed. Some of the other six-month students were contented with having passed and decided not to go on to do part two but to go back into General Nursing.

We had been together for only six months but I knew I would miss them all as we said goodbye.

AN INTERLUDE

We had a month's free time before starting Part Two Training. One afternoon Margaret said, "If Part Two is as hard as the last six months, we really need a holiday."

"We do," I said, "but how could we afford it on pupil midwife pay?"

Then I caught sight of an advertisement in the Nursing Mirror and rushed to tell her.

"This sounds just the holiday for us," I told her, pointing to the page.

I read the caption aloud, "The Edith Cavell Home of Rest for Nurses near Lake Windermere. Cost for a week, two pounds ten shillings."

"It could be worth a try, I suppose," she said, "At least we can afford it."

"It might be a change," I said and wrote to book a room for us.

A week later, our six months ended and we were more than ready for a complete change of scenery. We packed our belongings and books to leave at home and made plans to meet in Derby to travel to Windermere together.

Margaret had told a friend of hers about our holiday and Sheila had decided to join us and booked into a small hotel nearby.

It was a bright May Day when we arrived and made our way to the Home where we were shown to a second floor room by the housekeeper who gave us a list of rules we must keep. In defiance,

Margaret immediately lit up a 'coffin nail' as she called her Woodbine cigarettes. Not her favourites but the ones she found affordable. She stretched out on the moderately comfortable bed and relaxed.

The evening meal was fairly tolerable but insufficient for two nurses who had just finished a hard spell on the labour wards and we felt in need of nourishment.

However it was not to be at the Edith Cavell Home, for breakfast consisted of tea and cornflakes; not even a choice of any other cereal that we might have expected for the war had now been over for ten years and rationing was almost at an end. The other visitors were elderly and seemed quite satisfied with what was offered. We gathered that they did not go far from the premises so perhaps for them, the food was adequate.

After this meal, we went out to look for the nearest café to augment our diet thinking we might not have much spare money if we had to do this every day.

Later, we met Sheila who regaled us with talk of the huge breakfast she herself had eaten that morning.

We spent most of the day finding our way around the small town and walking beside the lake. At this time of year, there were not many tourists and we found the place quiet and did not meet any of the other visitors from the home.

As we made our way back later, a cold wind blew across the lake and it started to rain so we were glad to get back to our room.

It was then we noticed how cold it was and huddled under our bedclothes until time for the evening meal. This did put some warmth into our bones and we decided to sit in the lounge for a while. We abandoned this idea quite quickly for all the chairs were taken and drawn up close to the very small fire, leaving no room for us.

Back in our room, we looked out on the wet trees wondering why we had come to this dreary place.

"Some holiday this is turning out to be," I said.

"I suppose I'd better unpack," Margaret said and started to hang her few possessions in the wardrobe.

I heard a scream and thought for a moment that she had found it infested with spiders but this was not so for she reappeared clasping a small electric fire.

"Look what I've found," she said.

It took very little time to find a socket and plug it in, sighing contentedly as the warmth pervaded the room.

"There's more in there," she told me, "We could have another one."

"We'll have to be careful." I said. "I don't think we would be allowed to use them if they knew."

"Perhaps we should only use one and put it back in the wardrobe before going out in the morning."

"We must make sure it isn't hot. We don't want to start a fire," I said.

At breakfast, the elderly ex-nurses sat around presumably enjoying their breakfast for Margaret heard one of them remark on what lovely cornflakes they had. Afterwards, Margaret only had to say," Lovely cornflakes" to have Sheila and me in hysterics.

On Wednesday morning, Margaret decided she'd had enough of austerity and went to share with Sheila for the remaining days. Being short of money, I stayed until the end of the week when we all caught the train back to the Midlands.

The one highlight in this dull week was when we booked a coach trip around the district. This day turned out to be the one good day of that week. The sun shone from a cloudless blue sky and was reflected in the clear water of the lakes. This impression of the lakes we took away with us was one to remember during the next six months of "hard labour" as we worked at the second part of training to become fully-fledged midwives.

MIDWIFERY PART TWO

ANOTHER CHANGE

Heathfield Road Maternity Hospital was in the part of Birmingham known as Handsworth. This hospital was small and rather basic compared with the City Hospital in Derby.

Although having only a few lying-in beds, it could be quite busy. It surprised me to see the delivery room held two beds with only a curtain between them. Quite often, both beds would be in use together but the patients did not seem to mind; perhaps they were too engrossed in their own progress to worry about what was happening on the other side of the curtain.

The atmosphere in this hospital was informal and relaxed which made the pupils feel at ease. We were treated as if we were already experienced which was a good boost to our confidence. We were to spend three months here and for the remaining three months we would be on the district. Because Birmingham is a very large city, we would live with the midwife and work in her area.

The Assistant Matron, a Welsh lady, among other duties, was in charge of the catering at this hospital. She kept an eagle eye on the cook who had to keep up a good standard so after the frugality in Derby, we found the food excellent.

There were two other pupils, Joan with whom I would work again later and Frieda who was German and had been a draughtswoman before coming to England to work. As usual, we managed to have fun in our off-duty time when we were off together by exploring the area around. On one of our walks, Joan and I found ourselves outside the Greyhound Stadium and could hear shouting inside that made us wonder what was going on. We tried hard to find a place in the high fence to peep through but any cracks or knotholes were far too high for us to reach.

On one of these walks, we met the 'little nurse' from Selly Oak who lived in that area and was now working on the district. My mother was most interested when I told her about this.

There had been very few West Indian people in Selly Oak and Derby so I was surprised at the number there were in the Handsworth area. It was also a pleasant surprise to find that my old friend Dr.Taylor had not long left this hospital and had kept everyone there happy with his friendly manner.

Despite being small, Heathfield Road had its own antenatal clinic where we met the Obstetrician, Mrs.Dunlop. She was extremely knowledgeable and taught us even more about pregnancy, labour and post-natal care.

One morning in clinic, one woman had swelling of her hands, a sign of pre-eclampsia and Mrs.Dunlop decided to admit her for rest and observation. The patient was rather worried because her wedding ring had become so tight, she could not remove it.

"It won't have to be cut off will it?" she asked anxiously.

"Not if I can help it," was the reply.

I was asked to get a one-inch cotton bandage which was wound around the patient's finger from the fingertip towards the ring. The end was then, very gently pushed under the ring, and then slowly pulled, gradually bringing the ring down the finger as it unravelled. Of course if the finger had been much more swollen, this might not have been possible. The woman was very grateful, possibly because if the ring had been cut, it would be costly to have it repaired, in which case it may not have been mended. Many of our patients were poor and the extra expense of providing for a new baby meant they had little money to spare for extras such as this. Any woman with a baby and not wearing a wedding ring was likely to be ostracised at that time.

Night duty was a busy time as there were less of us on duty and babies always seemed to arrive at night. As one of the Midwifery Sisters said, "Well, most babies are conceived at night so it's not surprising they are born at night."

All the babies were taken into the nursery at night so that the mothers would not be disturbed. We had to work hard for often there were babies to feed and most needed a nappy change during the night. The nursery overlooked the busy main road and when I was preparing the babies for their first feed, I could hear the morning buses on Heathfield Road taking people to an early start at work.

On arrival at Heathfield Road, we had been issued with a brown gabardine raincoat and brown beret to wear outdoors. We had to wear this outfit on the trips to Birmingham city centre for a weekly lecture and for this, we caught the local bus service. Although we felt very nondescript in this outfit, there was an advantage. One of the local schools wore similar coloured outdoor clothing and because of this, we were often charged child's fare on the bus. Being so poorly paid, we did not feel guilty, for after all we were working for the local authority and felt that we ought to have been issued with a pass for this particular journey.

The hospital sisters helped us to consolidate everything we had learned earlier and we became more confident about our work. They were always ready to explain something we were not sure about and show us anything unusual.

Most babies were delivered with the mother lying on her back and the midwife standing on her right side. We also learned to deliver babies with the mother lying on her left side 'the left lateral position' for some women suffered excruciating backache which made it painful for them to lie on their back for any length of time. Generally though, when babies are eager to enter the world, the mother and midwife will manage.

Early one morning the ambulance brought in a woman in labour who was making a lot of noise, shouting, and screaming at her husband. He was a small insignificant looking man who seemed glad to be left to sit in the corridor.

We were surprised to hear that this was the fourteenth baby and the Sister said, "She was making as much noise as if she was giving birth to all of them at once."

We often found that with a first baby, the mother was too busy trying to get on with her delivery to make a great deal of fuss but surprisingly, the more babies she had, the more noise many women made.

I knew that soon I would be sent to the area where I would commence the part of my training on district. Although bicycles were provided, these were not always reliable so the next time I went home, I brought my own bicycle back with me. Luckily there was not nearly as much traffic in those days so my journey was not too difficult.

WORK ON THE DISTRICT

The first three months passed quickly; September arrived and the pupil midwives moved to various districts. Our rooms at Heathfield Road would be taken by a new intake of pupils. The district to which I had been assigned was on Trinity Road quite close to the hospital. The large house where the midwife lived had been converted into four flats. The upper two were occupied privately and two district midwives, Miss Black who was my supervisor and a midwife who did not have pupils, occupied the ground floor flats.

The right hand flat was the larger and had a room where stores were kept and our bicycles could be left safely. Miss Black had a car for which there was a garage at the back of the house.

It was a pleasant surprise to find another pupil midwife already installed there. Cynthia had come from Dudley Road hospital and after being introduced, she showed me round the flat. There was a cosy sitting room that due to our work, we rarely had the opportunity to use. The midwife had her own bedroom into which we did not go unless to tell her something of importance. Our own bedroom contained two beds and a cat who should not really be there. He escaped into our room if we left the door ajar. Nigger, a name now seen as racist, was jet black and very friendly; he knew who would give him titbits and a fuss. The drawback was that this was Birmingham before the clean air acts and his fur did tend to pick up the grime from the outside air. This meant that he left the telltale mark of his body, usually on Cynthia's bed which made Miss Black angry with both of us.

"I will come with you for your first three deliveries," Miss Black the midwife said. "If I think you are capable after that, then you go on your own."

This was an anxious moment, would she be very critical but as my training had been good, I decided not to worry.

It did not take long to settle in for I had not brought many possessions with me and was soon waiting for the first call. As it happened, it was not long before this came and I prepared to go out. It was quite a luxury to be driven to the small terraced house on the outskirts of Handsworth and knowing I would have to return on my bicycle to do follow up visits, I took note of the route taken.

Apparently this patient's GP liked to be present at confinements and he was already there waiting for us. The patient was quite well on in labour and after examining and preparing her for delivery, we waited for labour to progress.

Miss Black chatted to Dr Jenkins while I checked the number and duration of the contractions and encouraged the patient with her breathing.

Everything seemed to be going well when the lights went out and save for the flickering of a very small fire, we were plunged into darkness.

The harassed husband, Mr. Taylor came into the room.

"Has anyone a shilling for the meter? "

Having checked our pockets, we all replied "No!".

"I'll have to go and ask a neighbour."

"No you don't," said Dr Jenkins, "not before you find us some sort of a light, that is if you don't want your baby to be born in the dark."

Luckily, Mrs. Taylor's sister came to the rescue with a candle that gave out a flickering light and Dr. Jenkins stirred up the fire into a blaze.

There was now no time to worry for the baby was on its way and soon a little boy was safely delivered. Dr Jenkins examined him and said he seemed satisfactory but he would check him again in the morning in daylight.

Having waited for the placenta (afterbirth) to be delivered he checked on Mrs. Taylor and left us. At last, the long sought shilling must have been found and the room was flooded with light again. Not the bright light of a hospital but sufficient to check the baby and mother and make them comfortable.

After this, the placenta had to be inspected to make sure it was intact for if even a very small piece was missing, it could be adhering to the uterine wall and would cause bleeding. It was only rarely that this happened which perhaps was due to the relaxed atmosphere in the patients' homes. In those days, if we were sure the afterbirth was indeed intact, we had to dispose of it. This was done by wrapping it up well in newspapers and burning it on the kitchen fire. There was no central heating in most of the homes and a large fire was kept burning all day for boiling water and cooking. Nowadays, a placenta would have to be taken to the hospital for disposal.

We arrived back at the flat at eleven and after something to eat, I was glad to get to bed.

One morning two days later, a call came to say another woman was in labour and this time everything went well and I delivered a healthy baby. I felt pleased that my first two supervised deliveries had gone well. Now the midwife would only come with me once more and I would be on my own at deliveries unless I had to call on her for assistance.

Depending on how far the labour had advanced, if necessary, we could give Pethidine to the patient but often this was not needed as most women did not send for the midwife until the contractions were every three to five minutes.

We had just finished our midday meal the following Saturday when a call came to go to an address in Aston and as this would be my third delivery, I expected Miss Black to come with me. To my surprise she told me to go and she would call in later. This being a third baby, the mother having two little girls already, I did not expect any difficulty.

When I arrived at the house, before preparing her for delivery, I told Mrs. Jones that as I was new to the area, Miss Black would call in later. Labour progressed well to the distant noise from the Aston Villa football ground which was not far away. Labour progressed quickly and the second stage began but on examining my patient to see if all was well, I was surprised to find the baby's face was presenting. This was not a usual type of birth and could be difficult to diagnose. One of the causes of this type of presentation is anencephaly where the vault of the skull is missing. This was worrying but expecting Miss Black to arrive, I knew I must carry on until she did so.

"What is it?" the mother asked as she saw my face.

"Your baby is coming face first," I said speaking as cheerfully as I could so as not worry the mother. "I think he or she wants to see what's going on."

It was impossible at that stage to know if the baby was in this position because of an abnormality but there was nothing I could do except to reassure the mother and continue with the delivery.

We had been taught about the various ways the foetus could present in the birth canal but this presentation was quite rare, at that time about one in five hundred births, so although I had practised with the model, had not had the opportunity to see or deliver this type of birth.

Because of the excellent tuition I had received previously, I knew the chin must be born before the occiput which had to be held back. As this was not a first baby, I found the birth fairly easy to manage and in a short time a healthy girl arrived as the noise from the football ground grew even louder.

"That sounds as if the match is over," said Mrs. Jones.

"Perhaps your new daughter will be a football fan," I said, "she seems to be trying to make as much noise as those at the match."

It was a relief to see that the baby did not appear to have any abnormalities as I explained to the mother about the birth.

"Your baby is fine and does not seem to have any ill effects from her unusual position. I will ask the doctor to examine her to make sure she is healthy," I said.

Still the midwife had not arrived so once I had made mother and baby comfortable; I left just in time to be surrounded by the football crowds on their way home as I made my way back to Trinity Road.

Life on the district kept Cynthia and me quite busy, we each had our own patients to visit twice daily for the first five days and then once daily until we discharged them. We also had to do some of the housework in the flat and to check that we had plenty of supplies.

After each delivery, we had to wash and sterilise our instruments and pack the necessities for home delivery in our bags ready for our next call.

At about six months of pregnancy, the patients were asked to collect their delivery packs or if they could not manage to do this, to send their husband to pick it up. Without the pack, the midwife could not deliver their baby and they would be sent to hospital which few wanted. There were also gas and air machines which the mother could use if she wished. As these were rather heavy, when the woman went into labour, the husband had to collect the machine. They were rarely used as the only transport the husband might have was a bicycle but in their own homes with familiar people around, the women were more relaxed and most babies arrived without difficulty.

We had been informed by Miss Black that we were only allowed a half day each week but that instead of this, she would let us have a long weekend once a month. This meant we could finish at midday on the Friday and come back on Sunday evening. It did mean the pupil left behind was on call during the whole weekend and could be extremely busy. Despite these setbacks we enjoyed the work and managed to catch up on sleep whenever we could.

Most of our calls came at night either by phone or more often by a shrill ring of the doorbell. Some nights, I woke up being sure the phone or doorbell ringing had woken me, and find everything quiet. Then within a few minutes, just as I was falling asleep again, either phone or doorbell would ring loudly. When asked if the caller had rung before, I would be told , "No!" I often wondered if this was some sort of premonition as it happened several times.

Cynthia and I took it in turns to go out on calls but if one of us was already out, it was no guarantee that another call would not come. Often we were both out on the same night and one night, I came back to find Cynthia had been called out, and just as I settled down to sleep, I was called out again.

Most deliveries were straightforward and there was usually someone in the family to supply hot water, clean towels and cups of tea as needed. Occasionally, however, having first seen that we had everything we needed, the husband would disappear, returning only when the baby had been safely delivered.

We did hear of a pupil midwife left on her own at a delivery; she managed everything without a problem until after delivering the baby; she looked up and saw the two other small children watching intently. As she told us afterwards, "they had their first witness case."

In most cases, although we did not have any single mothers, if the husband was not available for any reason, there would be another member of the patient's family or a neighbour who would supply us with anything we needed.

One afternoon, I was called out to a woman in labour with her second pregnancy. All went well until the actual delivery, the first thing to do once the head is born, is to feel that the cord is not around the neck. If it is, quite often it can easily be pushed over the shoulders. In this case, the cord was so tight, it was impossible to do this. The only thing to do, was to cut the cord, quickly unwind it and clamp the ends to prevent excess bleeding. This was difficult but by pushing the rounded end of the scissors between the cord and the infant's neck, it was possible to cut, clamp and unwind it from the baby's neck.

As soon as this was done, the blood spurted out before the clamps were in position although this was done as quickly as possible. The baby was born after this and cried lustily, suffering no ill effects. This is the sort of situation that could be disastrous if the mother is alone without any help.

It was not often that we needed to call out our supervisor midwife but one night I went to Mrs. O'Brien who was having her fifth child. The house was poor and shabby and the patient looked pale and anaemic. The delivery went well, but afterwards, her pulse was weak and although blood loss was minimal, she looked even more pale. I thought she had lost more blood than she could tolerate as she looked so anaemic and sent the husband to ring Miss Black who in her turn rang the GP. Obviously, he knew this patient quite well and sent for the flying squad who came out promptly. They set up a blood transfusion and gave her one pint of blood quickly and a second one more slowly. The change in the patient's colour was dramatic and when the flying squad doctor was satisfied with her condition, they left.

As most babies were born at home, the flying squad which consisted of a team of highly trained doctors and midwives was based in the city. This team was alert and ready to come at a moment's notice to deal with all kinds of obstetric emergencies. They always carried a supply of blood as more often than not, this was needed. In the fifties, even in a large city like Birmingham, there was not nearly as much traffic as there is now and emergency services were rarely delayed.

Early the following morning, before starting my routine visits, I went to check that Mrs O'Brien's condition had not deteriorated. The door was opened by a nun who explained she was from a convent in the city. I had been worried because many of the mothers did not get any help, often getting up to look after their other children before they were really fit. It was likely that Mrs. O'Brien would try to look after her family and do more than would be good for her. The nun said she would stay for a month and look after the mother and children. The husband was nowhere to be seen and knowing he did not work, I could only assume that he had left everything to the Sister.

EXPERIENCES

We never knew where our next delivery might be; many people in Birmingham lived in small back-to-back houses consisting of two rows of terraced houses that did in fact, back on to one another. Each house had three floors; the ground floor in which all cooking, washing, not only of clothes but their own personal washing and general living was done. Above this was the main bedroom with a smaller attic room above. Whole families lived in these houses. If the house was at the front, it opened onto the street and washing had to be carried to the back through an entry to be hung to dry in the communal yard. Toilet facilities were in what was known as the back yard and were often shared by more than one family.

It could be very difficult for a woman to keep this kind of house clean especially when she had several children. Many of the houses were untidy or grimy but despite this, most families provided the necessities for a home birth. These were clean, and were usually ready at the pre-birth visit. If the mother had not made these preparations, she might have to go into hospital for the birth and no one wanted this. Quite often the patient had a mother or sister living nearby and if not, a neighbour was ready to come in and help.

Generally, the mothers preferred to have their babies at home where the atmosphere was much more relaxed. If there were other children, the woman was glad to be at home as leaving young children could be upsetting for both. It was always a delight to watch the other children being introduced to their new brother or sister.

After a busy morning, I had just finished my midday meal when the phone rang and as it was my turn to go, I collected my bag and cycled off.

This time it was to a large house let into one-room flat-lets and the patient was a young girl of seventeen living with her husband in the top floor of the house. It was her first baby and naturally, she was apprehensive so I did my best to put her at ease by telling her about everything I would need to do.

Although the furniture was sparse, the room was clean and the preparations for the baby were good. The patient's mother was there to help and to give reassurance to her daughter. On arrival, labour was well established and as the mother was young, the birth was easy. The baby, a boy, was a good weight and cried well as soon as he was born.

This is a moment that I always find quite emotional yet at the same time, rewarding. It is such a wonderful moment when a healthy baby is born, and all is well. Most mothers having their first baby were delivered in hospital but for some reason, this baby was born at home. Promising to call back later, I left mother and grandmother with the new arrival and went to complete my other visits.

The weeks went by and autumn days were drawing in; with the colder weather, it was often foggy too. One afternoon I was called out to a small terraced house in Handsworth, not far away from Trinity Road. This house was so clean it sparkled and smelled of lavender furniture polish. The baby clothes were wrapped in tissue paper and I could tell immediately that this baby would be welcomed. It was a first baby but labour progressed quickly to delivery. All had gone well and both parents were delighted with their little boy. Having made the new mother comfortable and resting, I started to bath the baby. As I did so, the husband brought in a beautifully laid tray with two cups, tea-pot and milk jug.

He put the tray down and poured the tea, gave one cup to his wife and placed the other on the tray.

"This is for you," he said. "After all you've done, you deserve it."

"How lovely," I replied, "but it's my job and it's something I enjoy."

I finished dressing the infant and handed him to his mother.

"Isn't he lovely," she said.

Turning to the tray that contained a lovely china cup of tea and a plate on which was what was known then as a 'fancy' cake.

"Yes, that's for you too," the husband said.

As by this time, I was quite hungry, I felt justified in spending a little more time enjoying this treat.

A little while later, having made sure that all was well with both mother and baby, I said goodbye, collected my bicycle from the kitchen where it had been placed and walked out into the late afternoon.

Although it was not yet completely dark, it was rather a shock to go out into a dense fog, for there had been no sign of it a few hours ago. I could not see well enough to mount my bicycle so set off walking slowly hoping not to get lost. The bicycle lamp seemed so feeble giving just enough light to see the curb at the edge of the pavement. Turning left at the end of the street onto the main road it was a relief not to have far to go. The light from the street lamps seemed distant but proved that it was the main road. Usually in those days, the traffic was light but as I pushed my bicycle along, I became aware that a car was crawling along the road behind me. Stopping to make sure my bag was securely fastened, the car stopped too. A voice asked whether this was a certain road and I said yes. The driver then asked if he could drive behind me as he then knew he was still on the road. I said he could certainly drive behind me if it would help him but I would be turning off soon. I don't know whether he found his destination; I had trouble finding my own turning but eventually arrived back safely..

There was no point in returning later to check if the new mother was all right and run the risk of getting lost in the fog. Early the following morning, the fog had cleared and I was glad on visiting to find all was well. At every visit to this house, the husband or his mother brought me a cup of tea; often with cake using what I was sure was their best china tea service.

Some of the patients were seen at an antenatal clinic but a few came to the flat to be examined. Cynthia and I did not see many of them for we were always out during the day making our follow up visits. One evening the telephone rang just as we were about to have our evening meal. A frantic father said their new baby would not stop crying and please would someone come as their own midwife was not available. Miss Black said I must go and see what was wrong. "Some of these new parents soon get upset," she said, "They probably need help with feeding."

I cycled off hoping not be long for I was hungry and ready for my meal after a long busy day. When I arrived, it was to find the baby's parents living in one room which was part of a very large old house. They were a West Indian couple but the room seemed full of dark faces that at first seemed rather menacing. It was very hot and the baby was perspiring and red faced, evidence that it had been crying for some time. There was a blazing fire in the grate and the cot had been placed close to it. The infant was dressed in a woolly jacket and covered with a thick blanket. He was much too warm and his crying had made him even more hot and bothered. It was an alarming situation as everyone seemed to be expecting a miracle. Feeling apprehensive, I knew it would be difficult to calm the situation. The young mother herself was crying and gave me a pleading look.

"Can someone get me a baby bath or a large clean bowl and some warm water," I asked as I lifted the baby from the cot.

"I'd like a towel and some clean baby clothes," I said to the baby's father who went to a cupboard and produced a clean towel and clothes.

Talking quietly to the baby, I removed his clothes and gently placed him in the water. Immediately the crying ceased, to start again once he was lifted out.

"I want you to give him a feed," I said to the mother, "He is probably hungry after all his crying."

Having dressed him in clean clothes, I gave him to his mother and helped her put him to her breast where he sucked hungrily. All this time I talked gently to him in a low voice and found that, young as he was, he seemed to be listening.

Soon he had finished, and becoming sleepy, was ready to be replaced in his cot. I noticed that the audience had drifted slowly away and the baby and his parents were now alone. Probably the other occupants of the house had come in to try and help.

"I know you have been told to keep your baby warm but sometimes they can get too warm," I told the parents. "We don't want baby to get cold, but we don't want him to be too hot either."

I removed the cot from its close position to the fire.

"Try to keep his cot away from any draughts," I said. "If the room gets cold, cover him with an extra blanket which you can take off if the room gets warmer."

By now the baby was sleeping soundly and the parents were happier.

"I'll come back tomorrow morning to see him," I said as I left.

Returning to Trinity Road, I found my evening meal that had been placed in the oven to keep warm was dry and unpalatable. Luckily, there was some bread so I made toast and found enough marmalade to spread on it. I was to get into trouble for this as it was intended for breakfast and I had used it all.

WHAT NEXT?

During these weeks on the district, a letter arrived from Anne with whom I had worked on the infants' ward at Selly Oak. She said there was a vacancy for a Night Sister at the Derbyshire Children's Hospital and why didn't I apply for it?

I thought this might be a change and even on permanent nights; at least the hours would be regular, also my pay would increase so I applied. A week or so later, I received an appointment for an interview and was offered the position which I duly accepted.

One night, we had just settled down to sleep when the doorbell rang to call one of us out. It happened to be Cynthia's call and I settled down as she left. It seemed I had hardly closed my eyes when the phone rang to call me to another delivery. All went well and although small, a healthy little girl was born. Everything appeared to be normal and after wrapping the baby in a clean towel, I put my hand on Mrs. Dawson's stomach to feel the uterine fundus and see if the placenta (afterbirth) had separated. We had been told in our lectures to wait half an hour unless there was excessive bleeding before calling for help. There was no sign of separation and I waited patiently but when after twenty minutes there was still no sign, I asked Mrs. Dawson's sister to call Miss Black. She arrived about ten minute later and decided to send for the GP. Doctor Clarke arrived and after he had prodded on the patient's stomach with still no sign of separation, he sent for the obstetrician.

It was now beginning to seem rather bizarre as well over an hour had passed since the birth when the specialist examined Mrs. Dawson and said, "You'll have to come into hospital."

He did not do anything about this and as there were no mobile phones in those days and few patients had their own phone, it often meant going to the nearest call box. It was important to make a mental note to remember where these were in case of an emergency.

Just then, the patient's sister who had been in the kitchen came in and asked if everyone would like a cup of tea. By now, it was about three in the morning and I was surprised when they all said, "Yes."

I turned to say to Mrs. Dawson that I was sorry but she could not have a drink but even as I looked at her, I noticed a change as she frowned.

"I've got a pain," she said.

I put my hand on her abdomen and immediately knew by this, that the placenta had separated. With a push, it was delivered and all was well although it was then over two hours since the baby had been born.

The obstetrician examined her, decided that everything was satisfactory, finished his tea, then he and the GP left.

"I think you deserve that cup of tea," I said to Mrs. Dawson.

Despite all the time that had elapsed, there was very little bleeding which, if it had occurred would have been a real emergency and required urgent action.

This incident shows that it pays to be patient and not to meddle as Miss Gorman, the tutor at the City Hospital always told us, usually, nature does know best. Had Mrs. Dawson's baby been born in hospital, after half an hour without signs that the placenta had separated, she would have been taken to the operating theatre and it would have been removed manually. Later, when I worked in an NHS hospital, I found that this was a routine undertaking. In this case, the placenta was intact and the patient recovered well.

Late one evening, I was called to a patient who lived in the Aston area but as I cycled along with my heavy bag fastened on the carrier; my front tyre went down with a hiss. The one thing I dreaded had happened, a puncture meant I had to push my bicycle the rest of the way. A flashing torch at the end of the road showed me that I was near my destination.

"What's happened?" the worried husband demanded as I reached him.

"I've got a puncture," I said, "but I must see to your wife first before I do anything else."

Taking my bag, I hurried into the house and up the stairs to reassure and apologise for being so long.

Luckily, although this was not a first baby and labour was well established, the birth was not imminent and I had soon prepared Mrs. Deakin for delivery.

"You mustn't take any notice of my husband," she said, "like most men, he gets in a panic when he can't do anything."

Everything proceeded normally and she gave birth to a little girl that pleased both parents as they already had two boys.

When I eventually left and went downstairs to collect my bicycle, I found that the puncture had been mended for which I was very grateful. In those days, most people cycled to work and so puncture mending skills and equipment were readily available. Even so, it was kind of him to repair my tyre when he was worried about his wife. I found whilst on district, most of the people, although many of them were quite poor, were always ready to help anyone with a problem.

Shortly after midnight when I had been on the district for just over two months, I was called out to a patient on the next district as the midwife was on holiday and we were on call for her. My destination was a small terraced house and this was one of the most grubby, smelly houses I had seen all the time I was in Birmingham. There did not seem to be anywhere to hang my coat so I spread some newspapers on a chair and put my coat and bag on this. I opened the delivery pack and placed the contents on a small table with newspaper below. The baby was born about four in the morning and was a good weight. I washed the mother and bathed the baby, telling her I would return in the morning.

The patient's sister brought in cups of tea but this was the only house during my whole time on the district where I left the tea untouched. The cup looked as if it had never been washed and was so dirty, I was unable to drink from it.

By this time it was almost five, I returned to Trinity Road, and after visiting the following day, was glad when the other midwife came back from holiday.

Another mid November day, I set out to do my follow up visits and found another thick fog covering everything and cycling slowly down the main street almost rode into a shop window whose light suddenly loomed in front and almost dazzled me. Without realising, I had ridden across the pavement where there was no curb. The fog was so thick; one could be very close before walking or riding into a hazard. I was extremely careful after this episode. Luckily, we did not have too many days that were as murky and gloomy and our time on district passed quickly.

On our weekly trips into town for the lecture, I was able to see Joan and exchange details about our experiences. She too had been placed with a midwife who left her to do everything on her own and rarely visited any of the patients.

At the end of November, we returned to Heathfield Road Hospital and prepared to take our Final exam which, like Part One, was held at Loveday Street in Birmingham. We were rather apprehensive about this, as we had to examine a patient and take her case history before having an oral exam with a Professor of Obstetrics and a Midwifery

Tutor. The patient who had been allocated to me was helpful, enlarging on her obstetric history as I questioned her. This helped me answer the questions given as correctly as I could. The professor asked many other questions and then the Midwifery tutor asked more. Although they seemed satisfied, I still felt worried about the outcome.

Afterwards we felt as tired as if we had been up all night and were glad to get back to the hospital and relax for the evening.

Just over a week later, our results arrived and we opened the envelopes hesitantly and then with relief found we had all passed.

Mrs.Dunlop, the obstetrician at Heathfield Road, told me there was a place for me there if I wished to stay but reluctantly, I had to tell her that I had already accepted a place at the Hospital for Sick Children in Derby.

"If you change your mind, let me know," was her reply. I would have liked to stay there but I wanted to extend my knowledge of Children's Nursing.

A few days after this, we said goodbye to everyone and for the first time in five years was able to spend Christmas at home.

NIGHT SISTER

THE CHILDREN'S HOSPITAL

Situated on North Street in Derby, this hospital trained nurses for the Register for Sick Children. Although serving a sizeable area, it was not large; the nurses were all at various stages of their training and enthusiastic about their work. The deputy on night duty was a Staff Nurse who had completed her training as a Children's Nurse and she was very helpful.

There was a pleasant nurses' home for the students but the sisters lived in a large house on the Duffield Road close to the Hospital.

Now at last the silver buckle my eldest brother had bought me when I passed my nursing finals could be worn.

After a few weeks, Staff Nurse told me that some of the nurses were not happy and were discontented about the irregularity of their nights off. Having taken over from someone else who had established a particular routine, I had not changed anything. It was unsatisfactory if the nurses were not happy; something needed to be done about it as soon as possible.

Every nurse was entitled to work five nights on and have two off with a third night off every three weeks. It was not easy to juggle with these figures but eventually, I sorted out a plan and took it to Matron for her approval one morning.

"I'm afraid the nurses are not at all happy with the way their off duty is arranged," I told her.

"Why is that?"

"Well, they often work more than eight or nine nights in a row and get very tired," I said.

"Well there's not much I can do about that. I'm sorry."

"I've been thinking about it," I told her. "When I was off at the weekend, I made a plan. There's one drawback though."

"What is that?"

"We will need one extra nurse on night duty but it does mean that when each nurse finishes her time on night duty, she will be back on day duty more quickly."

"It sounds all right but will it work?"

"Here is the plan I've made. I'll leave it with you to look at," I said.

When I saw Matron the next morning, she reluctantly agreed to try this plan and the following week, I put it into practice.

As it happened, there was a changeover of nurses, some moving to day duty and others coming to night duty. This made it much easier to implement the new system. It was good to see that the nurses who had taken over were quite pleased with the arrangement. It meant they knew when they would be off duty and could make arrangements if they wished. They also knew in advance, on which wards they were likely to be working and this met with the approval of the ward sisters.

There were many non-nursing duties expected of a Night Sister at the Children's Hospital; one of these was answering the phone and connecting enquiries to the various wards. The small office containing this very old system was situated near the front door in the entrance hall. Staff Nurse had shown me how the system worked and I had to learn this extra duty as quickly as I could. If a very ill child was involved, I could answer some queries directly.

Another duty was sorting out the evening meal but this could often be delegated to one of the nurses if I was occupied on one of the wards.

Although acute surgical or medical admissions could take place at any hour of the day or night, the casualty department was often quite busy in the evening. Late one Friday evening, a seven-year-old girl was rushed in having been bitten on her face by a dog. She was crying; her face streaked with tears and blood.

The wound was large, jagged and ugly; the mother was distraught.

"You've got to do something," she cried.

Luckily, there were no other patients waiting and while the doctor was examining the wound, the mother told us what had happened.

"We've just come from Leeds, it's my sister's wedding tomorrow. Jilly can't be a bridesmaid now. She's been looking forward to if for so long. It'll break her heart."

I did my best to calm the mother as she was upsetting her daughter even more. Meantime, the doctor called the Surgical Registrar who looked at the gaping wound carefully.

"Well, it's a nasty thing to happen but I'll do my best," he said to little Jilly. "I will have to make very tiny stitches which will help make it better."

"But she won't be able to be a bridesmaid now," wailed the mother.

"Of course she will, the dressing will cover it and the scar will hardly show once it's healed."

The mother sat down suddenly she was so relieved.

"Oh, thank you, doctor."

Now the mother had calmed down and Jilly knew she would still be at the wedding, the wound was stitched. The Registrar painstakingly used a very fine, light suturing thread and needle, suturing the wound with tiny stitches so I am sure the resulting scar would be hardly noticeable. A much happier and calmer mother and child left us.

On another evening, an eleven-year-old girl came in with nasty lacerations to her index finger. She had been wearing a small silver ring and had climbed onto the roof of a shed in the garden. All would have been well had she not slipped and caught the ring on a nail at the edge of the roof. This had torn the ring from her finger and in doing so had taken a lot of flesh with it.

She walked into Casualty with her mother who was scolding her loudly.

"I told you not to climb up there but you never do as you're told."

"If I hadn't slipped, I'd be all right."

"But you did and it isn't all right."

The girl was trying not to cry but her finger, which was wrapped in a tea cloth and had been bleeding quite profusely, did not look good. It was another tricky job for the doctor but somehow, he pulled the lacerated ends together and stitched the finger neatly.

"Next time you go out to play," I told her, "take any jewellery off first and leave it at home."

"Yes," she said but I doubt if she really took in what I said as she was still rather shocked about what had happened. Perhaps her mother would remember and remind her.

I heard later that the wound had healed very well and in time, the scarring would fade. The simplest items of jewellery that children liked to wear could be hazardous at times.

The ENT (Ear Nose and Throat) ward was usually busy especially after a day when a large number of children had their tonsils and adenoids removed. This operation is not performed as often today and was a messy and painful procedure for the children. We also had children recuperating after mastoid operations, something else that with the use of antibiotics is rarely needed nowadays.

The surgical ward was kept busy at night for admissions could take place at any time, this being the only hospital for children in the area. On occasions we might have to admit a badly burned child who required skilled nursing care. Loss of body fluid was a problem and it was important to replace this but often they did not want to drink. The day sister had discovered that they could be coaxed to drink pineapple juice which was nutritious and contained elements that aided healing. Most of them needed skin grafts and some older children returned many times for more operations.

On my way back to the hospital in February after nights off, I was about to leave home when I felt the earth under my feet shake. It was an odd sort of sensation lasting only seconds; my mother who had walked with me to the gate did not notice anything unusual. I dismissed the episode from my mind as I travelled to Derby.

However, when I reached the hospital, it was to receive a message to say a four-year-old boy was in theatre undergoing surgery. Little Paul had been out with his mother and sister when the earth shook. Although only minor, the earthquake had dislodged masonry and chimneys. Paul received a glancing blow from a chimney that fell from a building nearby and fractured his skull.

By the time I arrived on duty, Paul was on the ward and being watched carefully. Perhaps it was because he was so young, that by morning, he was much better and went on to make what we thought of as a full recovery. It was only later that I learned that this accident had left him with epilepsy. Apparently the earthquake measured five point three on the Richter scale so it was surprising that more people were not injured or greater damage done.

Recently, in two-thousand and eight, there was another earth tremor, which made many people recall the earlier one, and it was of interest to me to read an extract from a Derby newspaper about the earlier incident[2]. I was interested to learn that Paul had been diagnosed with epilepsy, which doctors said was a result of his injury.

There were some chronically ill children admitted for treatment that often could only be palliative, which was sad. We often admitted

2 Still Bearing The Scars Of City's Last Major Earthquake Back In 1957 By Kate Liptrot
09:30 - 28 February 2008

babies with Pyloric Stenosis, a condition where the muscle between the stomach and duodenum is too tight and does not relax to let food through. This often does not show itself until the baby is about a month old and then food is brought back in a projectile vomit. The infant loses weight and is fretful because it is always hungry.

An operation to ease this muscle is effective and the baby can be fed soon after recovery from the anaesthetic. It was found that if the mother could be admitted with the baby, she could feed him, (it was usually a boy) and the baby made excellent progress.

The paediatrician, Doctor Lawrence, at the Children's Hospital was one of the first to encourage the admittance of mothers and Ward Three, which held three adult beds, was reserved for this purpose. It could also be used to allow the parents of very ill children to stay at night.

A few months after I started work at the Hospital, my friend Joan came to work in theatre. Unfortunately, we did not see a lot of each other except when she was called out to an emergency at night. On rare occasions this could be dramatic and the skill of the surgeon who performed operations on tiny babies was remarkable. Twice we had very small infants with a stricture in the bowel that prevented food from passing through. This could have caused the baby to die. It was amazing to see how the narrow part of the tiny bowel was removed and the two ends joined together (anastomosis). Both babies recovered and began to thrive as now food given to them was fully digested.

We often had odd notes sent to Out-Patients explaining why an appointment had not been kept. These ranged from saying the letter had been eaten by the dog to one written on toilet paper with many apologies. Another was written on the back of the title page of a novel, another had disappeared under the lino in the hall only to be discovered months later when new flooring had been laid. One of the doctors kept these in a scrap book to be produced and shown to new doctors when they first arrived.

INNOVATIONS

During the time I worked at North Street, Doctor Lawrence obtained a supply of Salk Polio Vaccine which was difficult to obtain. He decided that those nursing sick children were some of the most at risk of contracting the disease and decided that all the staff should be vaccinated. He was probably right about the younger nurses for many of them succumbed to childhood illnesses they had not contacted previously. Often a child was admitted after an accident or for surgery and then developed measles or chicken pox. Those nurses who had not had the infection when younger often succumbed to these illnesses.

One night I received a frantic call from the nurse on Medical Ward Four and hurried to see what was wrong. When I reached the ward, I found a three-month-old baby who had been admitted that day, in a cot that was meant for an older baby. The danger of this had not been realised and as the infant became more active, he wriggled until his head slipped through the bars of the cot. This caused concern among the nurses. The senior nurse had placed a stool with a pillow on it so the baby's head was well supported.

This was where my obstetric training proved useful as I was able to gently manoeuvre the baby's head in the way learned how in the mechanics of labour, the head passed through the birth canal. This was successful and the nurses sighed with relief. In those days, if anything went wrong, even if not at fault, the nurse was often blamed and this could even lead to dismissal.

The months went by and in August, I received a message from my brother George to say his wife, Joan had given birth to a baby girl who was very small and had been transferred to the Premature Baby Unit at the Queen Mary Maternity Hospital. The following evening, the paediatrician came to see a child and asked if this baby was any relation.

"Yes," I said, "she's my niece. How is she?"

"She is doing very well," he replied."Come and see her tomorrow."

I did this and although Hilary was small, she looked perfect and was feeding well. I was pleased to let George know more about her as when he rang the hospital, they were only told that 'her condition was satisfactory,' not much to ease the worry of new parents. It was difficult for them to visit as Joan was still in a hospital which was some distance away from Derby in Ashby-de-la-Zouch so I was able to give up to date progress reports.

For quite some time, the Staff Nurse on night duty had wanted to start General Nurse training and after discussing this with me, she applied to a London Hospital and was delighted to be given a place in their intake the following year.

Before this happened, Christmas was approaching and I was informed that the night staff usually decorated the front hall. Someone suggested the theme of Hansel and Gretel for which we would build a witch's house made of dummy chocolate bars. A letter was sent to Cadburys telling the Management about our project and asking if they could help. A large parcel arrived a week or so later containing a dozen or so dummy bars and many chocolate wrappers.

Everyone set to work in their spare time covering pieces of cardboard with these wrappers to make authentic looking chocolate bars. These were stuck onto large cardboard boxes which we shaped like a house with a door and windows; the chimney was made of empty Smarty boxes.

PTS – I am on the tutor's left

1st Year Prize Giving

Prizegiving 1955

Children's Hospital with night staff

Prizegiving

Children's Hospital

QARANC February 1958 Intake

Left: Penny at Woolwich
Right: With Sheila outside BMH Gibraltar

Penny at BMH Gibraltar

Breda off duty

Corporal and Minnie

View of Gibraltar

Sugar Loaf, Gibraltar

BMH Gibraltar at sunset

On the way to the second temple

Hindu ceremony

Buffalo Cart

Kok Si Lo Temple, Penang

Two workers in a Padi(rice) field

One of the department stores in Derby loaned us two model children and a nurse made a witch riding on a broomstick which we suspended from the ceiling.

Being used to working over the Christmas holiday by now, I did not mind being on duty and enjoyed seeing the children opening their presents. Although I had loved working with the children, I did not like the idea of staying on night duty for several years and decided to look around for something else but few of the posts advertised stimulated my interest. Then one day, looking through a copy of the 'Nursing Mirror', I noticed an attractive advertisement for nurses to join the army on a short service commission in Queen Alexandra's Royal Army Nursing Corps (QARANC).

This looked interesting and as signing on for two or three years did not appear to be too long to commit myself, I decided to send for further details. I was not prepared for the speed in which things moved as before I could have second thoughts, I was invited for an interview in York.

The Officers' Mess was quite different to living in a Nurses' Home and I found the QA Officers very friendly. My interview seemed to go well as the interviewing board put me at ease and I decided to sign on for three years. After this, I went for the Medical Examination where I learned the minimum height required for entry was five foot, exactly my height.

During my interview, I learned that stockings of a shade known as "nocturne" were to be worn; a change from the regulation black in civilian hospitals. As usual, makeup had to be discreet and a special lipstick shade worn.

Back at the Children's Hospital I told the Matron what I intended to do. She was not very happy about this but I told her I would not give in my notice until I had a definite date for leaving.

It was several weeks before I heard anything and then I received a letter instructing me to report at the training headquarters in Hindhead near Liphook, Hampshire, at the beginning of February. After this I handed in my notice and told the nurses that I would be leaving soon.

Only a month remained of my time at the Children's' Hospital before leaving to start a new and entirely different life.

THE ARMY

QUEEN ALEXANDRAS
ROYAL ARMY NURSING CORPS

"You'll have to do square bashing." My younger brother David leaned back in his chair and grinned from ear to ear. "You'll love it."

My heart sank as I suddenly realised the horrors that army life might entail.

"There won't be much of that," I replied. "My time will be spent nursing."

"Everybody does square bashing. Wait until a huge sergeant bellows at you. You'll desert immediately."

"He wouldn't dare," I declared, "I'll be an officer."

My brother roared with laughter, "an officer, that'll be the day."

Having spent two years in the army on National Service some time before, he thought he knew everything. His teasing made me begin to have doubts and feel apprehensive about what life in the army would involve. It was too late to change my mind but I longed to extend my experience and this seemed to be the only way.

A week after this conversation, I arrived at the Queen Alexandra Royal Army Nursing Corp Depot in Hindhead.

The damp, dismal late February afternoon did little to raise my spirits as my taxi drew up outside a dark building where a solitary light shone.

What had I let myself in for, I wondered as I stood, luggage at my feet and gazed at the unremarkable front of this structure. I almost turned to ask the driver to take me back to Liphook station but already the taillights of his vehicle were disappearing.

I reminded myself that it had been a similar damp February day when I arrived at Selly Oak Hospital to start training as a nurse. Despite all the difficulties, the eventual outcome had been satisfactory otherwise I would not have been at the QARANC Depot that day. I lifted my suitcase and walked into the small reception area where warmth welcomed me.

"You'll have to live in barracks with lots of other people," my brother had said.

In the gloom of the late February afternoon, his words seemed to be confirmed as I was taken to a large army hut. Inside though, unlike the barrack room, my brother had described, it was divided into individual rooms rather like the wooden hut I had lived in some years before when I first started nurse training.

A round black stove stood in the centre of the hut; this gave out warmth to only a small area. The individual rooms were bitterly cold and everyone crowded round the monster to introduce ourselves.

We were quite a varied group of eleven nurses; all had joined the army in the hope of travelling abroad and using our skills in different places. The list of postings was enthralling and perhaps a little daunting but we were informed that we would not be sent overseas for at least six months. Our experiences ranged from one newly qualified nurse to others with several certificates and someone who had spent some years in the Kentucky Nursing Service.

After speculating on what the next few weeks would entail reluctant to leave the slightly higher temperature, we separated and went to our rooms to unpack.

Later, we were taken to the Officers' Mess where a huge fire blazed in the anteroom where we began to thaw before our evening meal. After this, we dragged ourselves back to the hut to settle ourselves in.

Woken by reveille the following morning, we went to the Mess for breakfast, after which we were given our first lecture on Army Law and Protocol as applied to officers in the Q.A.R.A.N.C.

Later that morning, in the Quartermaster's store we were each given a khaki battle dress in what was near our own measurements. As was to be expected, we were reduced to laughter as we looked a motley group when we tried these on. Some of the uniforms were baggy, others far too long and the skirts in danger of slipping over hips to an untidy heap on the floor. We were also given heavy black shoes; these were to be worn whilst in uniform. Major Jamieson, the officer in charge told us that tailors would arrive in the afternoon to alter each uniform.

After lunch, we had more lectures and I was surprised when Major Jamieson said that those who wished could smoke. This was in nineteen fifty eight and probably would not be allowed today.

At two that afternoon, several tailors arrived and adjusted the uniforms, taking them away to be altered and miraculously changed into trim outfits by the following day. The shoes supplied with battle dress were heavy and I hoped would not need to be worn often.

"Tomorrow afternoon you will wear battle-dress at all times except when you leave camp," Major Jamieson informed us. It was a surprise when we returned to our quarters after lunch the following day and found beautifully tailored battle dresses folded on our beds. At last, we would look as if we really belonged.

That afternoon more tailors arrived from London to measure us for number one dress uniforms. We also had to order grey ward dresses, black ward shoes, short red capes and veils, (squares of material embroidered with the badge of the QARANC) that are worn on the head. In addition, a grey, red lined cloak to be worn when necessary with ward dress.

The shoes sold to us by the tailors were much more comfortable than those given to us at the Quartermaster's store. They were soft but quite serviceable and I found later that they made very little noise. I was so pleased with these I bought two pairs as I knew I would always need good ward shoes. Finally we were measured for number one dress uniform and grey greatcoats. Although we received what seemed a generous uniform allowance, we were warned to be careful how we allocated this money, as apart from an allowance for tropical gear, all replacements would be paid for by ourselves. There was just enough left for a tin trunk to hold these items of uniform.

The following Friday, we were sent to the Medical Centre to be given several vaccinations; these were for the diseases that might be endemic in the areas to which we could be posted. Because it was possible that some of us might have a reaction to any of these, we were told we would be confined to barracks for the weekend. We could if we wished go for walks around the area but definitely not further afield. Apparently in the past, before this rule was initiated, one member of a previous intake had gone to London for the weekend and collapsed in Oxford Street which was not a good advertisement for the Army.

After our evening meal, we gathered together in the main building, thinking that this rule was hardly necessary as we all felt quite well. Then gradually, one by one, we began to wilt and feel unwell so that by the time we returned to our rooms, we were glad to lie down. In the morning most of us felt lethargic and were glad to stay around the area especially as the weather was rather bleak. The following day was bright and although cold, we went off in various directions to explore the surrounding countryside. By Monday morning most of us had recovered from any after effects and were back to normal.

On the third day, after an hour of General Information, we assembled on the barrack square, arriving as the Sergeant Major appeared. Our instructor was immaculate, not the red faced Sergeant David had warned me to expect. A man who would bawl at us and tell us what an 'orrible lot we were' in true British Army tradition but an extremely polite man who greeted us courteously. Over the next few weeks he must have thought we were the worst recruits he had ever met yet during that time he managed to instil the basics of drill into us.

"You will meet me here at o' ten hundred sharp every morning except Sunday," he informed us before we went for coffee in the Officers' Mess.

He soon had us in line. Unlike the 'square bashing', my brother had warned me about; this started almost at walking pace but soon became more arduous; walking quietly through hospital wards was not at all like this.

"Halt," he shouted and we stopped in ragged formation. "March like this ladies," he said as he paraded smartly up and down in front of us.

Off we went only to be stopped again. "Swing your arms alternately like this," he said, a twinkle in his eyes as he looked at Rae who had been swinging both arms together.

We marched, some of us turned right as ordered, others turned left, the Sergeant Major called us to halt.

"Now ladies," he said politely. "Try to remember which arm is right and which is left."

After being treated to another demonstration of the correct way to march, we tried again, this time doing just a little better.

At the end of the session, we were told to watch the 'other ranks' who were arriving for their training. They marched smartly onto the square, arms swinging in unison, demonstrating how drill should be carried out. We admired them although thinking it would be impossible for us to reach their standard in the short time we were at the depot. However we were unlikely to need this skill when working in busy hospital wards.

"Will *we* ever march like that?" Sylvia asked.

"I know I won't," said Rae. "Nor me," others echoed as we made our way to the Officers' Mess for coffee.

After the first session, my heels felt sore in the heavy shoes; would I be able to complete two more weeks without getting blisters? Then I remembered something Sister Andrews at Selly Oak had told me about surviving the effects of marching during the war. She assured me that rubbing soap on stocking heels would prevent blisters. It was worth trying and if it didn't work, nothing was lost. The next few days I followed these instructions and after each session my feet felt comfortable. Each day, I continued this treatment but in our last week, the weather that up until then had been dry, suddenly changed. Rain did not prevent our morning session on the barrack square and we marched up and down in passable formation.

Suddenly I heard a suppressed laugh behind me.

"Do you think she has caught foot and mouth?" I heard whispered behind just as we were called to a halt.

"That will be all now, ladies. Good luck in your postings," he said as with a smart salute he marched away.

As we made our way to lunch, I discovered what the laughter and remarks had meant. That morning, I had rubbed my stockings rather too generously with soap and this combined with the rain had turned the soap to a lather on the backs of my shoes. Soon after dismissal, I made a dash for the cloakroom to wipe away the remnants of foam before joining the others for coffee. Needless to say it became a standing or perhaps I should say a marching joke for the rest of my time at Liphook.

That afternoon we were given our postings. Mine to Woolwich, Rae to Cow Glen in Scotland, Sylvia to the Royal Herbert Hospital in Woolwich, the others to various other Army Hospitals. Rae and I met again six months later in Gibraltar where she was delighted to remind me of the 'foot and mouth' incident.

BASIC TRAINING

It was a new life.
An unknown future
lay bright, untouched
where anticipation clashed
with apprehension and won.
In this army game.

There were others.
Like me, eager, expectant
of a new experience.
Raw recruits in the
unknown territory
of this army game.

Remarkably resplendent
the soft spoken sergeant
greeted his officer recruits
with a smart salute.
'Welcome ladies, to
this army game.'

Instructing new officers
he spoke politely explaining
carefully what to do.
How innocent we were,
knowing little
of this army game.

Marching was part of training,
quite different from walking
up and down wards
eyes alert for our patients.
"Heads up! Eyes front", he said,
"This is not a game."

And he was right.
When postings came
our true vocation
to nurse and care
for the sick and wounded
would never be a game.

WOOLWICH

The Military Families Hospital in Woolwich was situated not far from Woolwich Arsenal where Sylvia, who had been posted to The Royal Herbert Hospital, had her quarters. This hospital, which dealt mainly with soldiers, would mean her work would be quite different to mine. The Families Hospital dealt with Army families though we also had civilian women booked for the obstetric unit. In fact there was very little difference from working in any other Maternity hospital.

Because the hospital was small, staff numbers were also low but apart from one other lieutenant , all were midwives. The other officers soon made me feel at home and the senior sister explained to me how I should reply to or address the Matron.

"No matter what you feel about the rights or wrongs of a situation, you must always say "Yes Ma'am, or No Ma'am," she said.

One of the others whispered, "Yes Ma'am, No Ma'am, Three bags full Ma'am." and everyone laughed.

Despite being quite small, the hospital always seemed to be busy. There were three wards, one for service wives, each about ten beds. There was a small ward for children although they were usually sent to one of the larger hospitals, The post-natal ward held ten beds in addition to one delivery room.

I soon settled into the routine and found that I was happy to be working as a midwife once again. The Obstetrician, Major Collins

RAMC was friendly and helpful, dealing with emergencies with sensitivity and efficiency.

It was just as Sister Tutor had said about the army and being a midwife but I did not mind this at all. It was good to be back looking after the women in labour and afterwards, caring for them and their babies. However, I did find the regulation 'veils' could get in the way when bending over a patient whilst examining them.

We took turns in assisting at the Antenatal clinics and in this way became known to some of the mothers we would care for later.

I had not been there many weeks when Matron decided it was time for me to take my turn on night duty. The non-maternity ward and children's ward were looked after by a student nurse from the Training School in Woolwich. The midwifery Sister on night duty was in overall charge of the whole hospital. This seemed to work very well as we helped each other when necessary. The midwife was in charge of the Maternity unit but at night, there was always a midwife on call who could be sent for if needed. This might only be necessary if two women were in labour at the same time and about to deliver simultaneously.

My first night was quiet and this gave me time to settle in and get used to the routine of running a hospital on my own. After all, I had worked mostly on my own whilst on district and this was not unlike those days with the exception that now the obstetrician was always on call at the end of the telephone if needed. I found that if I could get the babies fed and the mothers settled as soon as possible, then I could be ready for whatever might happen later in the night.

After several nights, I developed a routine; then early one night having delivered one mother of a healthy baby boy. I'd cleaned the equipment afterwards and placed it in the steriliser to be ready for use again.

I was writing my notes when the telephone rang.

"Have you a Mrs. Betty Dawlish on your books?" a voice asked.
I quickly looked at our booking list and confirmed that we had.
"Well, she's in labour and the ambulance is bringing her in."
"Thank you," I replied and replaced the phone.

It did not take long to take the instruments from the sterilizer and set up the labour ward ready for an admission. After this I went back to the office to finish writing my notes.

Returning to the ward to check my newly delivered patient, I was surprised to see the centre light of the in the ward reflected on the floor. This was rather strange until I realised that the floor was at least one inch deep in water. I turned to see Nurse Devenish just behind me staring in horror.

"It's my fault," she said, "I should have warned you."
"Warned me! What do you mean?" I asked.
"It's the steriliser. The water doesn't turn off properly and if it's not left to drain after use, it overflows."
"Well, I'd better go and empty it and then mop up the floor."
"I'll help," she said.

The layout of the hospital was unusual in that the Delivery room and sluice were at one end of the hospital with the sterilizer in a small alcove at the far end of the main ward. Between the delivery and the main ward, there was a small annex with a door that opened to the outside for admitting patients in labour.

Before long, we were both wielding mops but it was hard work and we did not seem to be making much impression on the amount of water on the floor. As yet the expected patient had not arrived. I went to the door and looked out but there was no sign of movement of any kind.

Inspiration came suddenly, there was a step just outside this door and if we could push the water through the ward doors towards this, it would cascade onto the road outside. Time was precious, the patient might arrive at any moment so we set to work, our mops changed to brooms and soon there was a stream of water cascading out of the hospital door.

"Thank goodness it's night time," I gasped to the nurse. "I hate to think what Matron would say if she saw this."

"If we can get the floor dry, perhaps she'll never know," she replied as with renewed energy we attacked the flood.

At last, we were mopping the remnants of water from the floor and hoping the heat from the radiators would help dry it completely.

I looked at my watch, still only three in the morning and as yet, the patient had not arrived. Preparation for the morning was still to be done so I went into the office to write what I could of the morning's report.

Time passed, four, five, six o clock; still no patient. I gave a brief thought about what might have happened, perhaps it had been a false alarm and the patient was snugly tucked up at home. There was no time to speculate as I set to work giving cups of tea to the mothers, changing their babies in the nursery and taking them out to be fed.

I was finishing my report when the phone rang.

"This is the 'Mothers and Babies Hospital'. Were you expecting a Mrs. Betty Dawlish to come to you?" The owner of the voice sounded rather annoyed.

"Yes," I said, "but she didn't arrive."

"Of course she didn't arrive because she was brought here in mistake and she was too far in labour to send her on to you."

"Is she all right?" I asked.

"Yes, she had an eight pound baby boy. Both well and we're sending them to you later this morning."

With that, the phone went dead and later, I was able to explain to the day staff what had happened." A mystery solved, I thought.

Going back to my quarters later that morning, I was pleased to see that the road outside the Delivery ward was dry.

What a night it had been but it might have been worse if Mrs. Dawlish had arrived whilst we were struggling to get rid of all that water.

Strangely, no one seemed to notice the damp areas in the corners of the ward and under some of the beds. I never knew if this was found out because a few months later, I was posted overseas and never went back to Woolwich.

HIGHLIGHTS

Another incident during my time in Woolwich was whilst I was on night duty, my younger brother David married Janet. Unfortunately as this was took place in Prestatyn it would be difficult to get there and return on the same day. I was sorry to be unable to go. On that same day Queen Elizabeth drove along the Circular Road near the hospital on one of her official duties. Matron ordered that all staff not on duty should go to see her.

A few weeks later, back on day duty, I walking past the office one morning when the hospital clerk called me and I turned to see what he wanted.

"How would you like to go to the Queen's Birthday Parade?" he asked.

"Oh yes, I would," I replied.

"It's Trooping the Colour of the first Battalion of the Scots Guards this year and should be very colourful," he said. "We are always allocated tickets so I can let you have one."

I asked Matron for that particular day off duty and this was granted so I could go. One of the other sisters, Joyce was also given a ticket and the necessary off duty and we both looked forward to this event.

On the day, the skies were cloudy and a light drizzle was falling but this did not dampen our spirits in the least as we made our way to Horse Guards Parade. We found our places were at the front to the left of the buildings where members of the Royal Family would watch the proceedings.

The foot soldiers were already lined up and were standing in front of us waiting for the ceremony to begin. My first thoughts were of disappointment for as it was raining, they were wearing grey capes. I could not help wondering if these would be worn throughout for the rain showed no sign of diminishing. If anything it was becoming heavier and was seeping under my collar. The Guardsmen must have been just as uncomfortable as we were. Even so, this did not diminish the excitement among the crowds around us as time moved on.

Then the sky began to lighten, the rain decreased and gradually stopped. The temperature seemed to be rising, then with a sweep like the waves of sea on a shore, the men simultaneously removed their capes to reveal their scarlet uniforms and someone hurried behind them to collect the capes. While this was happening, we had not noticed the time but now realised that it was almost eleven and time for the parade to begin.

We heard the clock strike eleven as the Royal Procession arrived. The parade began with the Inspection and the Queen rode her horse slowly down the ranks of the Guards before taking her place for the ceremony to take the Royal Salute. The day was now looking brighter but I was so fascinated with the colour and music, I hardly noticed except to remove my raincoat whilst keeping my eyes on the magnificent sight of the Regiment parading in faultless order. How very different to the haphazard way in which we had marched at Hindhead.

Watching the bandsmen weave in and out in the intricate patterns they had been trained to do was amazing; I wondered how they managed to play their instruments so well *and* keep in tune. As the last of the Regiment disappeared from view along the Mall, I became aware that Joyce was nudging me.

"I'm starving," she said.

Suddenly realising that it was a long time since breakfast, and I too felt hungry, I said, "Perhaps we should get something to eat."

The crowds were leaving now and we followed slowly towards the shops and restaurants. In my mind, I was still seeing the brilliant colours and hearing the music but it was time to come back to reality again. It was an event I remember and relive each time I watch Trooping the Colour on television.

On my day off sometimes I went into London and found that nurses were often able to get theatre tickets at reduced rates. One afternoon, I stepped off a bus in the centre of London and Dilys was at the bus stop. I knew she had started General Training in London and it was a pleasant surprise to see her. She had some time to spare so joined me for coffee. We went to the theatre one evening and saw Agatha Christie's 'Mouse Trap', which we found very entertaining. We also saw 'Free As Air' a musical by Julian Slade before Dilys went on night duty.

A week or two later, the hospital clerk called me as I walked past the office.

"I'm not supposed to tell you this," he said.

I looked at him wondering what he meant.

"Matron will tell you so don't tell her you already know."

"What do you mean?"

"You have a posting to Gibraltar, one of the best there is."

It was exciting to realise that now I would see something of the world but could not tell anyone until I was told officially.

A few days later Matron informed me that my posting had come through and it was to Gibraltar. I wondered what my parents would think of this but after all, it was not too far away. Even though the work would be similar, there would be so much to see and do there.

Before I left England, I had leave due; part of which I spent at home and part visiting my mother's family at Evesham. Afterwards I had to report to the Depot in Liphook. It was frustrating to be told I would have to wait for a passage to Gibraltar and that meanwhile I must work at the Cambridge Hospital in Aldershot.

This was a large General Hospital for troops and families with a Maternity hospital, the Louise Margaret, known to nurses as the 'Lousy Mag'. It was a disappointment not to be sent there as my experience in the army so far had been mainly in Maternity work. Each day, depending which one might be short staffed I was sent to a different ward. Nearly everyone I met there seemed to be waiting to go abroad and all were impatient to be away to their destinations. The work was not arduous but I too longed to be on the way to a new experience. Then when I thought I had been forgotten, news came that, together with three other nurses, I was to sail a few days later.

LEAVING ENGLAND

The following days sped by, as I made sure that my equipment and uniform were ready. Everything was packed into the tin trunk I had been issued with at the depot ready to be taken to the ship. At the depot, before leaving, I met the other nurses, Major Eva Swinburne, and two other junior lieutenants. Rae, who I had met previously at Liphook, who had postings to Gibraltar, the third was Erica, a Lieutenant who would stay on the ship, en route for Cyprus where she would stay for the next two years.

Arriving in Southampton, our ship seemed large though not nearly as large as the Queen Elizabeth birthed close by. We were to share a four-berth cabin which Erica might have to herself when we left the ship. Having decided which bunks we would have, we returned on deck to watch as the Queen set sail later in the afternoon. Surrounded by tug-boats that seemed to fuss around her like bees around flower blossoms, she slowly moved out of the dock and on into the Solent. We watched her until at last she disappeared from view and then stayed on deck to watch the sailors prepare for our own departure.

This seemed to take forever, or perhaps it seemed so because I was impatient to be on my way. Then at last our ship moved out while as we left, stirring music was played on the dock by a military band. This was not intended as a farewell to us but for the First Battalion, The Prince of Wales's Own Regiment of Yorkshire. They were on their way to Aden, where they would stay for a year. My feelings were a mixture of elation and sadness, elation because something new and exciting was beginning and sadness because I was leaving everything familiar behind. It was a wrench even though over the previous six years I had become used to living away from home.

Yet instead of feeling homesick, I began to feel excited at the thought of the new life ahead. Would I work on Maternity wards again or look after the troops? Whatever I had to do would increase my experience and being a junior officer, there would always be someone senior to advise me.

As I watched, the harbour slowly disappeared from view, the strains of music became more distant. We sailed down the Solent, past the Isle of Wight and the Needles, which stood out sharply in the rays of the setting sun. As it grew darker, I made my way down to our cabin to prepare for dinner.

The dining room was large; we stood at the door, wondering where we ought to sit. Then a steward appeared and led us to a table where the Chief Engineer sat, resplendent in uniform.

"Good evening ladies," he said, getting up and introducing himself. "Do sit down and make yourselves comfortable." He pointed to the seats positioned around the table. Just four of them, enough for us.

"I always feel more privileged than the Captain," he said. "He has to have the top brass at his table so I always make sure I have the nurses."

He proceeded to tell us about the ship and then to flirt with us all so that by the end of the meal, we were looking forward to the next few days. Later, on deck we watched other ships making their way towards England with lights blazing. Reluctantly we made our way down to our cabin for the night.

In the morning, the sky was grey and the sea became choppy; this caused many people to become seasick. Being nurses, we were asked to look after several WRAC other ranks, (Women's Royal Army Corps) and make sure they had everything they needed. It was not long before my companions also began to feel queasy and went to lie down on their bunks. I looked in on the WRAC women at intervals to check if they needed anything and then later, I too went to bed to sleep. Apparently, we were passing through the Bay of Biscay, which is noted for being stormy; it was not unusual to suffer from seasickness there. Perhaps it was because I was kept busy looking after others that I felt fine until the following morning. Then after I had checked on the WRAC service women to find they were all recovering, I suddenly felt quite sick myself and went to lie on my bunk. After a rest, I felt better and found that most people were recovering and looking forward to the rest of the voyage. Later that day, the WRAC service women were feeling better and were able to look after themselves.

GIBRALTAR

ARRIVAL

There was an unaccustomed stillness in the air when I woke the following morning, and for several moments, I wondered what was happening. Then as I became fully awake, I realised the ship had stopped moving. We had evidently arrived at our destination and were now at anchor.

Excitement surged through me as I glanced at my sleeping companions in the other bunks. What would life be like here on the Rock of Gibraltar? I was eager to know more about my destination; the others slept on as I watched them. I walked quietly to the porthole and looked out. Now instead of the rough grey sea and sky we had seen for the last few days, the sea now calm, reflected the brilliant blue of the sky. I could see a brown, sun baked coastline in the distance with white buildings scattered here and there. Although early, not wanting to waste one moment of this day I dressed hastily and left the cabin. The first impressions of the place where I would spend the next two years were important. It was essential to remember everything and keep it secure in memory.

The activity on deck was unheeded as my eyes were drawn towards the rock of Gibraltar towering through the morning haze. It looked impressive and it was easy to understand its importance in the past. As the mist cleared, the houses in the town became visible although a layer of cloud still hung over the highest point of the rock, sweeping along its length like a veil. This was the 'Levant', a cloud whose appearance usually meant high humidity. Already the air was getting warmer even though a soft breeze helped to cool the ship. It would probably be quite hot on shore.

In the harbour, dozens of small boats were milling around our ship. Crammed with colourful objects, rugs, dolls, toys, leather bags and other things to tempt tourists. Although, as I found out later, they were speaking in English, the voices of the occupants were difficult to understand as they called to the passengers to buy their goods. These items were hauled up to the deck in baskets and returned containing the correct amount of money.

Watching the rapidly changing scenes around, I was oblivious of time. A hand on my arm brought me back to earth with a start and turning, saw Erica beside me. She urged me to hurry because Eva was getting agitated at my disappearance and our luggage would soon be collected to go ashore. Eva and Rae would disembark with me later that morning and Erica, having fully recovered from seasickness would sail on through the Mediterranean to Cyprus. She could now enjoy the rest of the voyage and the activities that were to be organised to keep everyone fit. Apparently, this was one of the last troop ships used in peacetime to take service personnel to postings around the world.

Knowing our senior officer Eva, was inclined to be strict and not wanting to upset her, I hurried below to finish packing and have breakfast.

It was much later, after eleven that morning, and extremely hot when we left the ship. The Matron, Major Hope of the British Military Hospital came on board to welcome us, something unheard of according to Eva. A young medical orderly dressed in shirt sleeve order saluted us and checked our luggage on to the tender that took us ashore. Dressed in the unaccustomed khaki battle dress, I felt extremely hot and sticky but did not dare show my discomfort. The brim of my uniform hat cut into my head tightly and made it ache. The hotter I became, the tighter the hat seemed and the more my head ached. When I thought no one was looking, I surreptitiously pushed it up off my forehead.

At the quayside, our luggage was installed into an open top jeep. Matron ordered the surprised driver to take us for a tour of the Rock. Soon we were driving through the town gates which we were told, are closed each evening after the historic Ceremony of the keys takes place. This is similar to the ceremony that takes place each evening at the Tower of London. We passed the naval base in Gibraltar called HMS Rooke in honour of Admiral Sir George Rooke who saw an opportunity to capture the Rock in July 1704 with a large combined fleet of British and Dutch warships. Initially the city fathers refused to surrender but after landings by British marines and sailors they were persuaded otherwise.

We were driven upward, past the Moorish Castle, reminder of other occupations of the Rock. Then even further, towards the area where the Barbary apes live, but today there was no sign of them.

"They must be creating havoc in the town," the orderly said. "When a ship is in port, the apes go down the rock to see what is going on and snatch cameras, sunglasses or other items from the tourists. They are very mischievous and seem to know how much they can get away with."

It is said that if the apes ever leave the Rock, then the British will go too. Apparently, during the war, the Prime Minister, Winston Churchill was concerned because the ape's numbers were decreasing. He took steps to ensure no harm came to those remaining; even importing more to swell their numbers. The apes are on the ration strength of the fortress and important happenings to them, births, deaths and casualties are recorded in Army Part One Orders. When necessary they receive treatment at the Military Hospital where they are taken by the corporal in charge.

It was cooler as we drove down the hill, where a few trees relieved the starkness of the barren rock. We passed gun emplacements with cannon pointing over the harbour and towards Spain and the Straits. The names given to them were reminders of Gibraltar's past.

Stopping at one of these, the view was breathtaking; far down below, we could see the airport, with its narrow strip of runway, stretching out into the bay and beyond this, the sun baked Spanish mainland with clusters of whitewashed houses gleaming in the sun. It all looked enchanting to me and I was reluctant to leave but Rae dragged me away. Our way then took us through tunnels that had been bored through the rock by the Royal Engineers. It was strange yet exciting and any uncertainty about this new life was forgotten as the thrill of adventure surged through me.

We were told that one of the first things we had to do after arrival in Gibraltar was to sign the Register at the Convent. Originally, the convent of Franciscan Friars who had lived there from 1531 it had been the official residence of the Governor since 1728. Next door is King's Chapel, part of the original Convent, where various regimental flags are displayed.

On the way from the town towards Europa Point, we passed the Rock Hotel on the left and on the right, the Alameda Gardens, one of the few places on the Rock where there were flowers and trees. The Admiral lived further up the Rock in a house and garden with a large Magnolia tree in the grounds. Later, several of us were invited there to see a play called 'The Magnolia Tree' about the history of the house but I cannot remember it all exactly.

At Europa point, we caught a glimpse of the white lighthouse standing at the southernmost tip of Europe, the windows sparkling in the bright sunlight. As the whole of Gibraltar is only one and a half miles long and three quarters of a mile wide, the tour was really quite short and we soon arrived at the hospital.

My room on the first floor was comfortable with a balcony overlooking part of the garden. There was a wonderful view across the straits of Gibraltar to Africa where the Atlas Mountains shimmered in the midday heat. This scene would be enjoyed every day during two years on the 'Rock'. I stood looking out, thinking about the unknown future; there would be new people to meet, new friends to make and new ways to learn.

Off duty, there would be many different things to do and see. Yet these first impressions of Gibraltar would remain for perhaps they were symbols of even better things to come.

WORKING ON THE 'ROCK'

During the rest of the day, we unpacked before meeting the other QA sisters. On the following day our work commenced, mainly routine everyday nursing tasks that have to be done in any hospital. The Families Ward was my first destination; this had mainly children to care for and kept me busy. The patients varied from a child with acute eczema who had to be covered with a coal tar ointment and others with high temperatures that needed to be investigated.

Eva went to the Maternity Unit, as she was to take over from the Officer in Charge who had finished her tour of duty. Rae, who was not a midwife worked mainly on the Troops or Families wards during her stay. Working with children was always interesting although thankfully, most of them were not seriously ill. Any child or adult who was ill enough to cause alarm was flown back to England.

Besides nursing, I found that there were other duties in which we had to participate. One of these was Duty Catering officer for which two sisters were appointed, usually someone senior with a junior member of staff. I found this interesting though time consuming and learned more about how the extra money each member of the Mess had to contribute to the funds was used. Another duty was being Bar Member and this included measuring the amount left in each bottle daily, not an easy task, this could be difficult, as the amounts left never seemed to tally with what was supposed to have been taken.

We also had to take turns at being Orderly Officer which meant being available to greet and take care of visitors and make sure all the 'other ranks' were in their quarters each evening by a certain time. The QA 'other ranks' were mainly student nurses taking part of their training with us. Depending how far they were with their training, some were given the rank of Lance Corporal or in some cases, Corporal. This was reminiscent of the days at Selly Oak as a student nurse.

While serving there, a QA 'other rank' who had passed her finals and become State Registered was posted to us. Because Matron thought she should be given some seniority over the others, she promoted her to Sergeant. This meant that this nurse could be able to use the amenities of the Sergeant's Mess which were better than those of the lower ranks.

Their quarters were next to the main road and were surrounded by a low wall. This would not prevent any of them getting out and going wherever they chose after the officer had checked they were all there.

On my first day off, Eva was off duty too so we decided to do some exploring together. To go into town meant taking a bus and we were intrigued by the local one. This had a sign informing us that it went to Europa Point and Vice Versa. All the buses looked as if they had seen better days as they rattled along the road below the Rock Hotel and on into town. To return, the bus stopped outside Liptons Store in town and passed the hospital before continuing to Europa Point. Most of the buses had pictures or small effigies of the Virgin Mary hanging on the windscreen which danced around as the driver negotiated the bends in the road.

Being small, it did not take long to get to know Gibraltar: the shops in the town were full of interesting items and the town itself was fascinating. The people of Gibraltar were and I believe still are, intensely loyal to the British Crown and every shop had a large portrait of the Queen on the wall. There was a variety of shops full of goods of all kinds mostly intended for the tourist market.

Having walked through the town, we decided to go on towards the border with Spain. Seeing a wide-open space we started to walk across this although we thought we could hear shouting in the distance. Suddenly there was a deafening roar and an aircraft flew very low over our heads, much too close for comfort. Undeterred, we walked on but when we reached some buildings at the other side, an irate Air Force officer stopped us.

"What did you think you were doing, walking across the landing strip like that?" he demanded.

"We didn't know that we ought not to be there," said Eva.

"Didn't you see the red lights flashing?"

"We didn't know what they meant."

"A plane that was landing had to divert. You might have been killed."

"We only arrived a few days ago. We don't know about these things, but perhaps we should have been informed," said Eva.

He let us go on our way and we decided that this had been a lucky escape and were glad to be still alive. We were more careful about where we went after this episode.

On another day off, Thelma, one of the other sisters, took me to Catalan Bay on the other side of the rock. To get there, we drove through William's Way, one of the many tunnels built by the Royal Engineers. The bay was interesting with the beach quite busy but we soon found somewhere to sit and enjoy the sun. We had not been there long when a dark skinned woman in a faded floral cotton dress came to us. She evidently knew Thelma who introduced me and told me this was Theresa.

"Ah, another sister. From the hospital?"

"Yes, I arrived two weeks ago."

"I look after the sisters. Would you like some tea?"

"Yes please."

Theresa disappeared and returned half an hour later carrying a basket covered with a clean tea cloth. In it, we found a pot of tea and sandwiches. The payment for this was moderate but we were told not to tell anyone else, as she was not supposed to supply refreshments.

It appeared that Theresa did this for all the sisters from both the Military and the Colonial Hospitals in Gibraltar.

Later, I learned that the people who live in Catalan Bay originated from Genoa and had settled there many years before. On another visit, I was taken into a small church, which was built partly into the rock. There were some lovely statues and a sense of peace pervaded the whole place.

Catalan Bay was a favourite venue for days off and was easily accessible by the local buses and I often went there. The only snag was because of the height of the Rock, at about four in the afternoon, the sun moved behind the Rock and a shadow was cast over the beach. This was the signal to pack up one's belongings and leave.

The following week, my day off was once more the same day as Eva and we decided to take the ferry to Algeciras in Spain. We wandered around the streets and looked at some of the shops there. By midday, the sun was high and the streets below were becoming extremely hot so we were glad to have cool drinks and purchase some fruit of which there was an abundance. It was good to return to the ferry and enjoy the cool breeze on the water.

Not long after this, I was sent to the Maternity ward to work. On this ward, the sluice room which was positioned at the end of the ward had a wonderful view. Being high up, this room looked out over the harbour and beyond into Spain. Unfortunately, this view which sparkled in the sunshine could only be glimpsed whilst hurrying in and out. The ward was much too busy to allow for loitering as the patients or their babies needed attention.

I found all the staff on the Maternity Unit were friendly and helpful.

It was not a large ward, we only had about twelve 'lying-in' beds plus one antenatal bed but it was extremely busy. Our patients were wives of all three service members, also some whose husbands were civilians attached to the services. The ward was more relaxed than the servicemens' wards and the women were happy during their stay.

One day, at lunch, I was talking to one of the other sisters, Fiona who suddenly said, "I've met you before."

"I don't remember meeting you," I replied.

"The speech making contest at the Queen Elizabeth Hospital."

"I remember going there but I was so nervous, I don't remember much about it or anyone there."

We became friendly and as Fiona, not being a midwife, worked on the General wards, found that we often had the same days off and spent many of these together.

Being so close to Spain, we wanted to be able to go over the border and explore. To visit, we could either use our passports, which gave us four entries each year when we could stay overnight, or there was also a special visa called an eighty-day pass, which allowed one visit over the border, returning on the same day. Having this pass enabled us to go into the little town of La Linea where we could visit the hairdresser or take a picnic and get away from the confines of the rock. Obviously, everyone obtained one of these passes as soon as possible.

It did mean that transport was a problem but this was resolved when I could afford to buy a scooter as I now had more money and prices were cheaper on the Rock. It was not too difficult to learn to drive but before going into Spain, I had to take a test. This was not so easy because the scooter was large and I was only small but eventually I managed to pass.

We were glad to get away from the Rock whenever we could and look for a Spanish beach where we could relax and enjoy the sun. In the late nineteen-fifties, there were no hotels and very few tourists so we had the whole coastline to ourselves or so we thought. However, we often found that just as we were settling down, even though miles from anywhere with no one near, suddenly, two Spanish Guards would appear as if out of nowhere. They were quite friendly and interested in who we were and so on. This was the time before Spain became a tourist attraction so two English women were something of a novelty to them. This happened so often that we became quite used to seeing two civil guards appear as soon as we had settled down.

Many of the sisters found themselves different forms of transport, Rae bought a scooter and Eithwen, the theatre sister, had a small Fiat five-hundred car, which suited her well. We all found it amusing when the Hospital Pathologist borrowed it, for he was more than six feet tall. Somehow, he managed to squeeze his huge frame into this small car; I'm sure he found it more comfortable with the sunroof open.

NIGHT DUTY

Very soon after this, my turn for night duty came round and as in Woolwich, the midwife was alone in charge of the ward. There was always a midwife on call to help if there was a sudden influx of patients in labour. Obviously, because whoever was 'on call' had to be on duty the following morning this was avoided if possible. One morning, Eva reprimanded me for not calling the 'on call' midwife out to help after I had two deliveries close to one another. I assured her that would have called someone if it had been necessary.

Night duty consisted of twenty-one consecutive nights on duty and it was a relief to hand over at the end of this time. This was followed by seven nights off when it was good to relax and spend some time resting and exploring the area.

Soon after this, another sister arrived to join us. This was Captain Breda Farrell, who was a great asset to the maternity Ward. She was fun to be with and worked hard yet managed to keep us entertained throughout her stay. When we were particularly busy, she used to say, "It's time they had television on the Rock to give the families something to do instead of keeping us so busy."

Yet she never seemed to mind staying to help or coming back after her evening meal if we were busy.

Later, Major Julie Lester arrived and with her, Lieutenant Sheila Sisson, another midwife. Julie was always complaining that Gibraltar was too noisy and she wanted more P and Q, (peace and quiet) which we tried to give her by trying to be quiet whenever we could.

The Officers' Ward was opposite the Maternity Ward but was rarely very busy. It was not long before the National Service Orderly who was on duty there at night came and asked if there was anything he could do for me. He originated from Preston and was a helpful, friendly man.

One night he told me the following story,

"Captain H. the Medical Officer asked me to get him an auroscope," he said. "I didn't know it was an instrument for looking into ears so I got him a copy of a magazine with horoscopes in it."

"What did he say?" I asked.

"He was not very pleased but I told him how was I to know what he meant? I'm a plumber?" he laughed.

He was, like so many of the National Servicemen who worked at the hospital, very pleasant, making the best of their new situation. One man was a trained Pharmacist who was sent to work in the Pharmacy and given the rank of sergeant while another who had been a medical student was promoted to corporal and worked in the Pathological Department. Others worked on the wards or were classified as General Duty Orderlies (GDO's). We often called on them to wash down the Labour Ward walls and ceilings when necessary. There was no difficulty in obtaining their services as at the completion of the work, Breda always gave them a bottle of beer each to drink before they left. These were sent to the ward for the mothers who were breast-feeding but few of them liked beer so there were always several spare bottles.

Work on the Maternity Unit was enjoyable and because Gibraltar is so small, we often met patients and their families in the town. This made our work even more interesting as some of the families were there for two or three years so that some often came in to have a second baby. One night, I delivered a young woman of a stillborn baby girl; a very sad occasion but a year later when she returned in her second pregnancy I helped her deliver a healthy baby boy which delighted both of us.

The maternity staff took it in turns to go to the antenatal clinic and this was helpful in getting to know patients before they were admitted in labour. The obstetrician, Captain Wright was very helpful and would be on the ward at a moment's notice if needed. He was able to gain the confidence of any patient who was having problems and was very kind to them all. Everyone had complete trust in whatever he found necessary to do.

One night, a woman in labour was not progressing at all well and the baby was becoming distressed. At that time, we did not have the monitoring equipment that is now available and had to rely on listening to the foetal heart with the stethoscope and examining the patient. I decided to call Captain Wright before the situation got worse.

As I was preparing for a forceps delivery I knew would probably be necessary, the doctor walked into the ward.

He made it seem like an ordinary visit as he asked the patient how she was feeling and told her he would just examine her to check how things were.

"I think I'd better give you some help with this baby," he said and went to ring for the anaesthetist whilst I finished getting everything ready. Before giving her the anaesthetic, the doctors put her at ease. It was not long before the baby was delivered and both mother and baby were well when the doctors left.

For at least twenty-four hours after a forceps delivery, it was the practice to 'cot nurse' and handle the infant as gently as possible. This allowed the baby to recover from the stress of delivery and then generally, there were few ill effects.

On my days off after this night duty, I went by train into Spain to a place called Ronda which stands on a promontory of land surrounded by high cliffs. Whilst there I stayed at a hotel that stood near the edge of a cliff, where there was a wonderful view down into the valley below. Looking down and watching the people below going about their work was fascinating and I spent a lot of time enjoying this outlook. The town of Ronda itself had many very old Spanish style buildings where I wandered and took photographs.

Although being on my own, I enjoyed my brief holiday and returned to work once more feeling refreshed and rested.

Night duty came around frequently, as there were only a few of us and we had to rotate; also, one of us might be sent to another ward at short notice to help out.

Once more it was again my turn for night duty and Eva told me that the Matron-in-Chief, Dame Monica Johnson, was coming to pay us a visit. I was on my third night when Eva said that someone had heard Major Hope tell Dame Monica that the maternity Unit was never very busy.

I think the fates must have overheard this for the ward was already full when I arrived on duty that night with one mother who had just delivered..

"We have transferred some of the mothers over to the Officers' ward. They are up and about and will be going home tomorrow or in the next few days so will be all right there." I was told.

However, this now meant that the only available cot would be in the labour ward and should be kept for any new babies.

Before she went off duty, Breda told me, "Mrs. Rowan's husband was told years ago by a clairvoyant that his wife would die in childbirth. The foolish man told his wife and she is frightened *she* will die whilst having this baby."

"Well, if everything is normal she should be all right," I said. "I'll do my best to reassure her."

"If you need any help, let me know," and Breda went for her evening meal.

I had scarcely started my routine work when the phone rang to say that another woman in labour would be in shortly. The problem was we had only the labour ward cot, which should be kept ready for the next baby to be born. This was a dilemma but remembering my time on the district, I knew that many babies started life in a drawer and I quickly emptied one in the side ward and cleaned it for the impending arrival.

The new admission was well on into labour and everything went well and soon her baby was born, a healthy little girl who was placed in the drawer.

"She's not the first baby to start life in a drawer," I told her mother, "and probably she won't be the last."

Whilst preparing the labour ward for the next patient, the phone rang to say another patient was on her way. In Gibraltar, no one lived very far away and the phone had hardly been put down when this new patient appeared.

Mrs. Jones was only in early labour so everything necessary was done and she was given sedation. Having made her comfortable in the last remaining bed, I showed her where everything she might need was kept, telling her to ring the bell for me if necessary.

"I've another lady in labour who will probably have her baby soon but I will come to you as soon as I can," I told her.

I then found that Mrs. Rowan was progressing rapidly in labour so transferred her into the labour ward. Although she did seem rather apprehensive about what would happen, I talked to her and kept her informed about how her labour was proceeding and she became less worried. Now there was the problem of finding somewhere to put her baby when it arrived.

As I hurried between wards, the orderly from the Officers Ward asked if there was anything he could do to help.

"Yes," I told him, "go to the Families Ward and see if they have a small cot or something I can use to put a baby in. I've already had to put one baby in a drawer so see what you can do."

He disappeared and I checked on Mrs. Smith who was now sleeping and then went back to Mrs. Rowan who was soon into the second stage of labour. She was a healthy woman and her baby was born normally shortly afterwards. There were no complications and I left her enjoying a cup of tea whilst I went to see whether the orderly had been successful.

On the corridor, I found a large doll's cot and hurried to disinfect and make this ready for the new arrival. Transferring Mrs. Rowan to the ward and settling her into bed, gave me time to check on the progress of the new admission. She was still sleeping so obviously not too far advanced in labour. Knowing how quickly things could change, I knew another delivery should be prepared for, so I cleaned the labour ward ready for when it might be needed.

At last, morning came and with it, the day staff who were quite amazed at what had happened but congratulated me on having coped so well with an unusual situation.

This was not the case with Major Hope who seemed quite annoyed because I had made the best use of what was available. I think this was probably because when she brought Dame Monica to the ward, it would show that the Maternity Unit could actually be quite busy.

After Dame Monica left us, I received a ticking off from Major Hope because I had acted improperly in my methods of finding somewhere for the babies to sleep. However, she did not give suggestions as to what I ought to have done.

One night I delivered a much wanted, very premature baby girl who appeared healthy. These infants, whose parents had difficulty in conceiving, we called 'precious babies' for they were wanted so much. She was placed into a warmed cot and I watched her carefully throughout the night. Later in the morning, she took a small drink of water hungrily. Before going off duty, she was sleeping and breathing well.

Sadly, going on duty the same night, she had died; perhaps if there had been an incubator for her, she might have had a better chance.

Several times, when premature babies were born, we felt the need for an incubator. Despite several premature births, we were told that the number of babies born who might need one was not sufficient to warrant the expense. The incubator might not be needed for months and would stand idle most of the year. Luckily the Colonial Hospital in town were willing to loan one to us but this had to be requisitioned and transported to the Military Hospital which took vital time.

In the summer months, Gibraltar could be very hot but because of its location, we found that there was usually a cool breeze blowing through the Hospital Wards. It was only once during my stay that I found the heat almost unbearable and I think this was when the 'Levant' was hanging over the Rock causing very high humidity. The patients also found the heat intolerable and we tried hard to help them keep cool.

PLAY ACTING

One day, Fiona said, "how do you feel about joining a drama group?"

"I think I would like that," I said, "Why?"

"Jane, the Red Cross Worker has called a meeting to find out who might be interested. Shall we go?"

"I don't see why not," and as we were both off duty we went to find out more.

At the meeting, Jane took charge and we began to feel that she was tending to tell everyone what to do. She was much too bossy and if she were in control, we thought few people would want to stay.

"Perhaps you could arrange a date for the next meeting," she said, adding, "I will leave you to get on with it as I can't take part. I must go now."

We all sighed with relief as she left leaving Eric, a Staff sergeant from the Education Corps in charge. He seemed pleasant and capable so we were quite happy about this.

There were others from the Education Corps, several people from the hospital, and some from REME who were based at the workshops in a tunnel at Europa Point. After discussion, we opted to name ourselves, the Europa Players.

At the next meeting, Eric brought along some plays for us to look at and we decided on our first performance. This would be Blythe Spirit by Noel Coward and after auditions, Eric and his wife Edna played the Considines, Fiona played the first wife and I was given the part of Madame Arcarti, the medium. Others helped with prompting, understudy and stage management.

Rehearsals took place whenever we had off-duty together and gradually the play took shape. It was a change from ward routine and we all enjoyed doing something different. Also, we were meeting new people from different areas of the army. We were a mixed group, all interested in Amateur Dramatics and we noticed that having promised help if needed, Jane did not come to rehearsals.

One of the group was Arthur, a corporal in REME, who became the stage manager. He often had to reprimand me in the play because, as Madame Arcarti, when the lights needed to be switched off, I had to go to the side of the stage where the light switch was supposed to be situated and say 'lights.' This was the cue for him to switch them off but the problem was that when I said this, in my enthusiasm, I was often nowhere near the side of the stage and the lights were switched off when I was in the centre. Eventually I did get this right and then all went well. Despite these minor problems, we became friends though at that time, neither of us realised our friendship would develop into something more.

On the evening we decided to actually perform, among the audience was the new Colonel of the hospital who said how much he enjoyed our performance.

The following day, Fiona and I were off duty together and decided to go over into Spain to spend the day. Unfortunately, our day ended rather abruptly when we skidded on the road which was rather rough with many potholes.

Both of us were hurt though not seriously, for as we came off the scooter, Fiona bumped her head and I had several large bruises that looked worse than they actually were over the next few days.

We were taken to a police station to give a statement which was rather difficult as our knowledge of Spanish was not good and the

Spanish Police Officer could speak very little English. On the whole, they were quite kind as I think they were not sure about what they should do with two Englishwomen.

Eventually we were allowed to telephone the hospital in Gibraltar and tell them what had happened. Jane and one of the drivers came to pick us up and take us back where we were immediately put into hospital for a few days.

Over the next days, we had several visitors from the drama group who had feared the worst when they heard about our accident. Once we were fit again, Fiona and I were glad to be back with the group to start rehearsing the next play Eric had decided would be a good one for us. Night duty intervened at times and as this could not be changed, we often had to let someone else take our place.

There were several flourishing drama groups on the Rock and each year a Drama Festival was held in Ince's Hall. This large Hall had been called after a Sergeant in the Royal Engineers. During the time I was in Gibraltar we entered with a One Act Play called 'The Telephone Never Rings'; although we did not win, it was an enjoyable event.

Unfortunately, because of night duty, I was unable to perform in another play which was 'Father of the Bride.' One of the others involved with the group was Mary, a sister who worked on the General Wards. She was able take the leading female part and I know she enjoyed this.

After rehearsals, Arthur and I met several times although we had to be careful, as officers were not allowed to associate with 'other ranks'. As we were both keen on photography, we enjoyed discussing how to achieve the best results. As time went by, I felt my feelings for Arthur growing deeper but I did not know how he felt about me.

We were not the only ones breaking rules as two other sisters were seeing RAMC corporals. Although the Rock was small, it was not difficult to be discreet especially as our friends were unlikely to say anything to our respective Commanding Officers.

The group worked on other plays too but because of changing duties I was not always able to join them except to help with 'off stage' duties.

At Christmas we performed a short play as part of a concert which consisted of men from the RAF dressed in drag, causing a lot of hilarity. Fiona and Audrey danced a Flamenco accompanied, by a Gibraltarian lady who attended rehearsals. I remember that during these rehearsals she continually shouted at Audrey to 'Smile Audrey, Smile," but in the end, all went well. Breda sang a song with actions that, judging by the applause, everyone enjoyed.

Several other members of the forces performed amusing sketches that met with applause from the audience so the evening ended well.

INCIDENTS

During my service on the 'Rock' Major Hope went on a long leave to her home in Australia. She was replaced by a Lieutenant Colonel who was very friendly, treating everyone as being an expert in their own field and rarely questioned a decision made on the wards by senior staff. Also being keen on photography, she sometimes invited me up to her flat to show her work to me and look at mine. She liked to take films of the area and people when she was off duty.

As much of the 'Rock' was barren, we felt privileged because there was a colourful garden in front of the QA Officer's Mess. From this garden, steps led up to the front door. Because of the shortage of water, it was difficult to keep the garden looking as it should but Julie had made herself its unofficial guardian. Often, when coming in late, she could be seen flitting among the flowerbeds giving them a surreptitious drink with water she assured us was recycled and had first been used for washing.

At that time, all the bath water came from the sea so to have a bath, we had to use this and then rinse off the salt with a jug-full of fresh water. This often left us feeling slightly sticky so often it was better to take a 'strip' wash in our rooms where fresh water was available. Because it rained so infrequently, we had to conserve water as much as we could. Water often had to be brought in by tanker to supplement that which was 'caught' in the 'catchment' areas on the 'Rock'. Huge sheets of corrugated galvanised iron had been placed on the steep

Eastern side of the Rock above Sandy Bay. Rainwater ran down these into a reservoir inside the Rock. Now, in the twenty-first Century, because of desalination, these are being dismantled.

During my stay on the 'Rock', we heard there had been an earthquake in Morocco at a place called Agadir and some of the staff were put on 'standby' to be ready to go and help with the injured if needed. After a few days, it was decided that extra help would not be required after all.

Coming off duty one evening, I walked into the Officers' Mess and saw a stranger chatting to those other officers who were off duty.

"Penny! Come and meet Paul Gallico," matron called.

I had read some of his books so was interested in getting to know more about him. We sat listening to him, enthralled with what he had to say. He was invited to our evening meal where we almost forgot our hunger as we listened to his stories. He had come to the 'Rock' to find out more about the apes. Writing a book about the part played by the Barbary Apes during the war, when because the numbers of the apes were diminishing, Winston Churchill decided to increase moral by importing more from Africa.

Having come to learn more at first hand, Paul visited us frequently. During his stay in Gibraltar we found his conversation fascinating. He was not a handsome man but so enthusiastic about his work, this did not matter as we listened and watched how animated his face became as he talked.

One day, Rae and I went with him to the Out-Patients Department to see Minnie, one of the apes who had been brought in by the Corporal in charge for treatment. Minnie had been in a fight and one of her hands had been damaged. Because of this, she had to be kept away from the other apes in the pack as they do not like a member of the pack to have an injury and might have attacked her.

After the treatment had finished, Rae decided she would like to have a photo taken with the little ape and held her whilst I took the picture. By this time, it seemed that Minnie had decided that she'd had enough excitement for one day and emptied her bladder down the front of Rae's ward dress who handed her back to the Corporal very quickly. We could not help laughing and this upset Rae but I told her it could have been much worse.

Some years later, I was able to obtain a copy of the book written by Paul Gallico which he had called 'Scruffy' and enjoyed reading it very much.

Occasionally, we held a party at the Mess for various dignitaries who lived on the Rock and Officers from the other regiments and Corps. One such was while Major Hope was away. Eithwen was in charge of the drinks and decided that a large bowl of punch would be a good idea. She may have got the proportions of alcohol wrong or perhaps someone else added more in mistake for many of the guests seemed rather unsteady. Matron was worried that they might fall down the steps outside but all was well. She said afterwards that she had never known a party go so well or seen so many Senior Officers so shaky on their feet. This party was remembered as one of the best held at the QA Mess for a long time.

One evening Breda and I went into the town to Casemates Square to watch 'The Ceremony of the Keys' a procedure that has taken place ever since the British have been on the Rock.

The tradition began during the Great Siege when General Sir George Elliott, the then Governor, carried the keys of the garrison at all times, even said to sleep with them under his pillow. Since then, Governors carry the keys on official functions except when handed over daily to the Port Sergeant for the ceremony of opening and closing of the gates of Gibraltar.

At least once a year, we had to have a ward check of all our supplies and this involved a visit by the Colonel, Matron and Quartermaster.

The senior ward sister joined them and all our equipment was laid out so each item could be counted down to the smallest teaspoon. All the linen, even used sheets and other items were counted and those in use on the beds were turned back so they could be counted more easily. If an item was missing, we had to search for it until it was found for if not, it had to be replaced and paid for. Luckily, we always managed to ensure that everything was complete and the lists signed by all concerned until the next inventory.

This type of check was done all through the army, even in the soldiers' and Officers' quarters but usually only when someone was moving out or in. This was known as 'Marching In' or 'Marching Out' and as I found out later, every mark such as a cigarette burn was noted down.

It was not long after this that Major Hope returned from her long leave and reluctantly we said goodbye to her replacement.

One Saturday morning, soon after this, from a window in the Officers' Ward, Breda watched Major Hope walk up the road towards the town. We were not busy that morning but even so, I was surprised to see Breda take a bucket of water and a stirrup pump to the window at the end of the Officers' Ward.

Just across the road was the RAMC Barrack block and Breda knew that most of the men would be having a long lazy lie in. It was only a little more than the width of the road to the open window of the block and Breda began to pump the water out of the bucket across towards the window. Before long she hit her target and angry shouts sounded across the road.

As the water petered out, faces were seen at the window but when they saw who had given them the soaking, they disappeared from view. We did not hear anything more about the incident so I think they forgave her. There was a spirit of friendliness among all who worked in the Hospital and the areas around. No one wanted Matron to find out, for if she had, there would have been trouble for Breda and probably me too as an accessory.

The atmosphere in the town was always friendly toward us, the people there always made us feel welcome and 'at home'. Perhaps the reason was because Gibraltar was so small, In the Main Street, people greeted me so that it was pleasant to wander around the town. It was interesting to explore the streets away from the main thoroughfares when off duty. One of the other sisters introduced me to a dressmaker who made me some lovely dresses for a very modest price.

Thelma was friendly with a pilot in the RAF who often brought back a crate of milk on his trips to England. This was especially welcome for we were not able to obtain fresh milk but had to use something called 'Supermilk', a reconstituted substance which some thought made tea taste unpleasant. Usually we drank our tea with lemon instead so to have 'real' milk was a bonus.

I was told that the man who invented this milk mixture was a millionaire having made his fortune from selling it on the 'Rock'. Obviously, many people did find this 'milk' reasonably palatable for him to make so much money.

Although our main duties were to care for Service personnel and their families, on occasion, we did admit civilians who naturally had to pay for their treatment. One such was a woman with a severe reaction after eating shellfish in Spain and was in my care on one of the instances when I worked on the Families' Ward. She was extremely ill with a high temperature and badly swollen eyes and face. With treatment and nursing care, she eventually made a full recovery.

On another spell of night duty, this time on one of the troop's wards, I looked after a young soldier who had met with an accident in Spain where the roads at that time were not very good. He had serious head injuries but was recovering as he waited for transport back to England. He did not sleep well at night and wandered round the ward, often coming into the Ward Office where he was given a drink of tea before one of the Orderlies took him back to his bed. He had suffered concussion that left some brain damage and would be given a full assessment and appropriate treatment on return to Britain. I often wondered whether he eventually made a full recovery.

Working on other wards helped me to keep in touch with new treatments. On another occasion, a child who had been taken to theatre during the day for tonsillectomy started to bleed in the evening. The bleeding became severe and the ENT surgeon, a civilian, was sent for but could not be found. To make matters worse, it began to rain heavily, so much so that there were floods in the town which made it difficult to reach the child's parents in the block of flats where Navy families lived.

Eventually, the surgeon was found and the child taken to theatre where his tonsils were re-sutured and all ended well.

OFF DUTY INCIDENTS

An interesting way to spend a day off duty was to take the Ferry across to Algeciras in Spain. Standing on the deck watching the Rock receding, strange activity was going on. It was amazing to see the passengers emptying their bags and disposing of the contents in a most unusual manner.

One man was arranging packets of cigarettes around his legs, fastening them with an elastic band and pulling his socks over these, he then took off his jacket to add an extra pullover. Women were dressing themselves with extra skirts and jumpers and despite the heat, putting on a large coat over these.

Arriving at the Customs Department in Spain, these people were let through with only a cursory glance. It was probable that the officials were bribed to allow this. Outside in the streets away from the harbour, some were ridding themselves of their superfluous clothing and replacing the items in shopping bags.

At that time, duty on many of these items was very high so it was lucrative for both 'smugglers' and customs officials as pay was very low. This trade would end when a few years later, the border was closed. This closure badly affected the Spanish people who worked on the Rock for they lost their income.

In the hospital, we had many workers who came from over the border and who enjoyed working for us. On the maternity ward, our maids were Dolores, Angela and Aurelia who had worked there for several years and came over from Spain daily.

In the QA Mess, one of the maids, Rita had worked there for many years and consequently had become very attached to the Sisters. When she was about to leave us for family reasons, we decided to give her a present to remind her of the time she worked for us. She said she would like a clock and this was bought for her in town and taken to her home in Spain.

In the 'winter' months, though we did not have any frosts, the weather was cooler which made walking quite pleasant. On my day off, I often walked up the Rock from Windmill Hill as far as it was possible to go to admire the view. At that time part of the upper Rock was out of bounds and the Cable Car did not exist. From being quite barren in the summer, many wild flowers bloomed during the colder, wetter months. During these months, the rain could often be heavy but was rarely wet enough to cause floods such as on the night we had difficulty in finding the ENT surgeon.

When I had been in Gibraltar for several months, I became due for some leave and decided to visit Granada, a place I had read about which had always intrigued me. To get there, I travelled by train from La Linea which in itself was an interesting journey through countryside that was quite dry and barren. It was rather like the countryside in parts of the United States; later I learned that many cowboy films were actually made in that area.

In Granada itself, I stayed at a Hotel in the main part of the town and spent most of my time exploring the area. The Alhambra was one place, I had always wanted to visit, having read, 'Tales of the Alhambra' by Washington Irving many years before and at the first opportunity, I made my way towards the entrance.

However, there were many distractions on the way in the form of small shops, that sold intriguing inlaid boxes, which tempted me to buy one for my mother. As I walked out of this shop, a guitar was being played; further up the street, the sounds becoming louder until stopping to look at various stringed musical instruments displayed in a shop window, a voice called to me in Spanish. Inside the shop, a man was skilfully playing one of the guitars and gestured me to sit down and listen to his music.

He finished playing and carefully placed the instrument on his workbench, and then showed parts of other guitars that he was making. It was easy to see that he loved his work by the way he picked up the parts and showed me how they fitted together. Despite my poor Spanish, I was able to understand what he was trying to tell me. Reluctantly leaving at last, I walked on up the hill to the entrance to the Generaliffe gardens where the water in the fountains sparkled in the winter sunshine. It was cold, almost frosty yet fresh and invigorating. The water comes from the Sierra Nevada Mountains and the Moors had designed the whole of the gardens, centuries ago.

I walked on into the Palace of Granada to see the beautiful courtyards where fountains sparkled in the sunlight and because, at that time of year, there were few tourists, it was quiet and peaceful. I was delighted to be able to take several pictures as I wandered around in this unforgettable place. Soon my leave ended and I went back to Gibraltar and soon became involved once more in the day-to-day work of the busy Maternity Unit.

We found that many things were cheaper in Spain and this included visits to the hairdresser in La Linea. Quite often two of us would go over the border to relax in Mario's salon where the assistants were pleasant and helpful. It was also possible to have a manicure whilst having our hair washed and set which was pure indulgence.

During the afternoon, we found most of the shops in Spain closed for the 'siesta' but after four, everything came to life. A trip across the border after duty could be interesting. As the time passed, by nine in the evening it seemed that everyone finished work and all paraded up and down the main streets in what I assumed to be their best clothes. Even quite young children were out with their parents. After the heat of the day, though still warm, the air felt pleasant.

On other evenings, as the sun sank, the rays coloured the Rock so that it changed to a warm pink which disappeared as the sun went down. In the evening, Arthur and I found it pleasant to walk down to the lighthouse at Europa point, then on through the tunnel at Arow Street, at that time restricted to Services Personnel only, and past the water catchment area. If the moon was rising, this shed its light on the sea giving it an almost ethereal appearance.

The road ran on around the Rock towards Catalan Bay where the lights from the houses shone out and reflected in the water. The next part of the walk led through another tunnel, Williams Way, and then on towards the town.

In town if not too late, it was possible to travel the rest of the journey by bus.

One night, whilst waiting for the bus we heard someone say, "There it is!"

Everyone was looking up into the night sky and we wondered why.

"It's the Russian Space Ship," someone told us and we looked up to see a faint twinkling light moving across the night sky far above.

We did not know then that this would be one of many attempts to go into space and eventually reach the moon.

One Wednesday afternoon, I was off duty in my room when I heard a strange noise which was loud enough to make me curious. On walking onto my small balcony, I saw a group of nuns walking down towards Europa point. I realised that the noise was from at least twenty pairs of feet on the road and the voices were the nuns chattering together.

Later, I found out that they were from the convent in Town and nearly every Wednesday, several had an afternoon off. Most of them went for a walk down to Europa Point which was a good place to enjoy the view across the straits.

THE NUNS

I heard a murmur faint and far away,
a sound like waves upon a shingled shore.
Then drawing nearer, synchronising with
the beat of feet upon the rigid road.

These were not soldiers marching off to war
but convent nuns released from daily tasks.
One day each week allowed to leave their work
and take a few brief hours of liberty.

For me, off duty for an afternoon
I stood and watched the nuns pass by and thought
about their lives, wondered why they should wish
to live secluded, in their chosen faith.

They called themselves the sisters of the poor,
and did not ask for wealth but gave their care
to those in need. Sick in mind and body,
were given help and healing through the years.

As dedicated soldiers follow rules,
so they too, were devoted to their cause.
They left the world's temptations, when they made
their vows and gave up all they had to God.

Yet with their peers, united for a time
like eager children at the end of school,
away from convent rules, they too, could talk
together and confide their hopes and fears.

Now, after many years, it seems I hear
them pass my gate once more. Voices made faint
through passing years. Yet memory lives on.
The vows they made, now only known to God.

SURPRISES

Very few of us knew of a certain incident until after it happened but it had some implications for several of us as leave had to be cancelled.

This is what happened; I was awakened late one afternoon whilst on night duty by laughter outside. Intrigued by this, I looked out.

Below my room on the terrace, I could see a group of nurses and one or two male army officers. I went downstairs to discover the cause of the merriment and excitement.

"Mary has just got married."

"She kept it quiet." I said.

"Well she didn't want anyone to know until afterwards."

"Who has she married?"

"It's a subaltern from one of the Regiments. She hasn't known him long and goodness knows what Matron will have to say about it all."

Meantime, they continued drinking champagne and toasting the newlyweds.

Apparently, it was possible to marry on the 'Rock' at very short notice and it was only needed to take birth certificate, passport and any other documents to the Registry Office the day before you want to marry.

In those days, it was protocol for any serving soldier or officer to ask their Commanding Officer for permission to marry. Neither of them had done this and consequently were likely to be in trouble.

The following morning Eva told me that Matron had relieved Mary of duties and she was to be sent home on the next available transport; no one knew what happened between her husband and his commanding officer.

Of course, it meant we were short of one sister and all leave was cancelled. I was due for my nights off a few days later and had planned to go to Morocco with Arthur to take photos and see something of the country. Our friendship had grown into something deeper over the months we had known each other and we both looked forward to this holiday together to get to know each other better.

The Assistant Matron told me of this change of duty and when my spell on nights finished, I went on to day duty straight away.

"But I've made arrangements to go to Morocco," I said.

I must have looked as disappointed as I felt for she glared at me and said,

"Who have you arranged to go with?"

It was impossible for me to tell a lie so I said, "I'm going with a friend, a Corporal in REME. We are both interested in photography and it's an ideal place to take pictures."

"You know it's not allowed for an officer to go out with an 'other rank'?"

I stood there waiting for her to say she would have to report me to matron. Would I be sent back to England in disgrace? Then before she could say more, I said, "He is due to leave for England in a few weeks."

"In that case," she said, "I will let the matter rest."

Perhaps she thought that to send two officers home in 'disgrace' would be just too much or felt that liaisons between nurses and 'other ranks' were inevitable as long as nothing worse happened.

Obviously, this also meant that Mary's involvement with the Drama Group came to an abrupt end needing some reshuffling to fill her place.

A few weeks later when a replacement arrived, I was able to take my leave. Unfortunately, I had to go to Morocco alone as Arthur was not able to change his leave. He did tell me of some of the places I might visit so in the end my trip was not too much of a disaster.

I enjoyed walking around the colourful souks and taking photos. So much was on sale, ranging from leather goods to carpets and blankets. There were colourful spices, fresh dates and figs to enjoy. I was able to take a taxi out of Tangier and see some of the countryside and a small town called Chaouen where I spent some time wandering through the streets. I took photos here but because the local people were superstitious about having their 'image' stolen, I was only able to take pictures of streets and buildings. Although for only a few days, this visit was a new experience and a complete change from Gibraltar.

Soon it was time for Arthur to leave the 'Rock' and we said reluctant goodbyes, promising to write to each other.

My turn for night duty came again and on my nights off, I went into Spain, spending a few days in Malaga where I visited the old Roman Amphitheatre and some of the Moorish buildings.

Afterwards, I stayed at Marbella which at that time was an unspoilt fishing village with very few tourists. An ideal place to wander through the streets and along the seashore and take even more pictures.

Back in Gibraltar, I knew my time there would soon end, although in England, I would meet Arthur again. It was still rather sad to leave the 'Rock' that had been my home for two years. One evening, walking through Library Square in town, I realised how much it would all be missed.

About this time, an RAF Officer, a Wing Commander, came out to referee some important cricket match that was to take place in Gibraltar. Unfortunately for him, when the match was over, he succumbed to a heart attack and had to be hospitalised. His wife came out and stayed with him until he recovered and was pronounced fit enough to be taken back to hospital in England.

As I was now due to go back to England, it was decided that I should go with him as escort to be available if he should be taken ill again. One afternoon in August, having packed my trunk with most of my belongings to be sent to my next posting, we left the 'Rock'.

Our flight to England was to Gatwick and having seen the Wing Commander into the ambulance that was to take him to an RAF hospital, I went to find my brother George and his wife, Joan who had come to meet me. They were living in the Manor House in Beaulieu where George worked for Lord Montague.

It was good to spend some time with them in the pleasant countryside around the New Forest. Hilary was now a lively three year old and although still small and petite, was fit and well. George had booked a holiday in Cornwall and we spent several days enjoying the sea and sun.

Back in Beaulieu George went back to work, for at that time, Lord Montague held several 'pop' concerts and George had charge of the money collected. As the Bank was closed at weekends, he had to bring a large sum of money home until the Bank reopened the following week. Joan was worried about this as she thought someone might want to steal the money and there wasn't a safe in the Manor House. Her solution was to hide it in the large disused oven where it was safe until taken to the bank the following week.

Soon it was time to go home to see my parents and to meet Arthur once more. He was now stationed at Manobier in South Wales and had arranged for me to stay nearby in Tenby.

We had a few days together there and then travelled back to the Midlands so that I could introduce him to my parents. It was while we were there we became engaged and decided to marry when my service in the QA's ended. But before this, I had three months left to serve and these would be at Catterick.

CATTERICK CAMP

After the sunshine of Gibraltar, Catterick seemed bleak and unwelcoming. It was now October and the dark evenings did little to relieve the gloom as I unpacked and settled in. Later, it was a pleasant surprise to find Sheila, who had been in Gibraltar with me and Erica who I had met previously on her way to Cyprus had also been posted to Catterick.

The living quarters at Catterick were old style army huts similar to those at the Depot. These were divided into separate rooms and were not too far from the Hospital which consisted of similar huts linked together by a maze of corridors.

Once again, Sheila and I found ourselves on the Maternity Unit but we were rarely on or off duty together. I found myself working with a Captain who was not very friendly and seemed to find the most unpleasant jobs for me to do. It was good to be on night duty again where my past experience proved to be useful.

The weather during those months was damp and cold, a complete contrast to the heat of Gibraltar. Only the thought that I enjoyed working with the mothers and babies, and this, only for a few months, relieved the gloom.

Receiving letters from Arthur, my parents and brother George was a pleasure to which I looked forward.

Here at Catterick, the patients were mainly the wives of Army personnel living in Married Quarters at the camp. However, when it came to having babies, there was no difference between a private's or a Colonel's wife, all received the same treatment and care.

Most pregnancies and the delivery of the baby were normal. This meant that apart from some of the mothers being anxious to go home to their other children, the ward was usually very happy with a pleasant atmosphere.

One day, I was sitting in the mess after dinner and one of the other sisters, a Major, was telling everyone that she had just received her new posting which was to Gibraltar.

"But I shall write and tell the locating officer that I don't want to go there."

"Why not?" asked one of the others.

"Well as a posting, I know Gibraltar will always be there so I'd much rather go to the Far East."

I was surprised at someone turning down Gibraltar which was considered one of the best postings. Some time later, I read that the hospital in Gibraltar had been handed over to the Navy and the Army would not return. When I heard this, I wondered if this Major had regretted her decision.

One night, I admitted the wife of an RAMC Corporal, a Mrs. Taylor, who was about thirty-six weeks pregnant with ante-partum haemorrhage. Her pregnancy had been without incident until slight bleeding occurred a week previously. She had been told in the clinic to come into hospital if bleeding started again. During the night she had woken and having discovered she was bleeding quite profusely, had come straight into hospital. The foetal heart was normal when she arrived but the persistent bleeding was worrying as this could be due to placenta praevia which is when the placenta, (afterbirth) lies too close to the cervix, (neck of the uterus). As the cervix dilates, this can cause bleeding which in some cases can be very severe. I put her to bed, reassured her and said she must not get up but ring if she needed anything.

After this, I rang the doctor who prescribed a sedative and said he would come in later. During the next few hours, I watched Mrs. Taylor carefully and listened to both mother and baby's heartbeats and both remained satisfactory. Having not long left her, it was a surprise when she rang the bell. She thought the bleeding was getting worse and this was confirmed on examination. Although the situation was worrying as the foetal heart was now becoming irregular, I reassured her then rang the doctor again but still he said he would come in later. By this time, it was more than likely she would need a Caesarean Section so I rang the sister on call to alert her. By now, the mother was getting restless and her pulse was fast. I rang the doctor again to inform him about the situation, also to let him know that the theatre staff were on alert. How I wished that Captain Wright the MO in Gibraltar had been there for he would not have needed ringing more than once.

Meantime, an incubator for the baby who would be premature had been prepared and the other sister was informed about what was happening. At last the doctor arrived and confirmed that Mrs. Taylor needed a Caesarean Section. She was prepared and taken to theatre. I followed with the incubator ready to take the baby and bring him or her back to the ward.

Although he was small, he did seem healthy and I was able to reassure his mother when she returned from theatre herself. Just before I went off duty, her husband who had been away on duty that night, came to see her and the baby. Eventually both mother and baby were able to go home, both having recovered from their ordeal.

Time passed quickly on night duty and I was glad of nights off to do some Christmas shopping in the local town of Richmond.

For the Christmas holidays, many of the staff were able to go home for a break. The camp seemed deserted each morning as I went on duty; the weather was even more bleak and cold. A small parcel arrived just before the holiday containing two books from Arthur. One was called, 'Carry on Nurse' with cartoons about mistakes made by student nurses. These cheered us up and caused much laughter in our off duty as Sheila had not been able to go home for the holiday either.

By the end of January my three years service would end and I had leave due and would be going home to prepare for our wedding.

Two weeks before this I had to see the Matron who asked what I would do after leaving the army. She wished me well as she dismissed me.

The last weeks flew by and soon I was on my way home with the good wishes of my colleagues to speed me. One had promised to lend me a veil to wear for my wedding and later this arrived at my home.

Apart from enjoying my work on the Maternity unit, I had few regrets on leaving Catterick. It was so good to be on my way home to prepare for my new life. There would be much to do during the next two weeks but I did not have any doubts about the future.

CHANGES

A DIFFERENT LIFE

On arriving home, there was a lot to do in preparation for our big day. Time rushed past but eventually everything was arranged. It was not to be on a large scale as we did not have the means for this but we wanted it to be a day to remember. On arriving home, I could not resist asking my father if he had that large medal ready to give to Arthur. He laughed about this and said he would think about it.

One of the first things to do was arrange for a special licence as Arthur and I would not be together for the calling of banns. We were to be married in the Baptist Chapel which I had attended for many years when living at home. This was in the nearby town where I knew many of the people including the organist who consented to play for us. The Minister agreed to perform the ceremony and as the chapel was only certified to solemnise weddings, I had to arrange for the Registrar to be present. It was a lot to organise but as I wanted everything to be as perfect as possible, this was most important.

Having arranged the necessary details, the next thing needed was a wedding dress. My friend Joan had consented to be bridesmaid and having arranged a day off, she met me in Derby to choose something to wear. Both being only about five feet tall, we decided on mid-calf length dresses which were in vogue at that time. It was exciting to visit the shops and after being away from the luxury of large department stores for a while, it was pleasant to see the variety of dresses. We did not have difficulty to find something suitable for the occasion and it was not long before we found a similar styled dress for Joan. This could be worn afterwards for special events. With the veil loaned by one of the Sisters at Catterick and shoes, our outfits were complete.

My mother had not given any thought about what she might like to wear so although she was reluctant, I went with her to choose a wedding outfit. We were able to find a smart suit in which she looked good and felt comfortable.

The time passed very quickly until on the twenty-sixth of January, Arthur arrived from Manorbier. The following day was a cold but sunny day with blue skies, the sort of day giving a hint of summer that sometimes comes in January. We went together to buy flowers and took bunches of lovely yellow daffodils to brighten the chapel. Later that day, Arthur's friend, Jim arrived to be Best Man and stayed that night with Arthur at the house of a friend of my mother.

On the twenty-eighth of January in complete contrast to the previous day, it poured with rain all day. Despite this, nothing could dampen our spirits and everything went well.

Many years before, I had been bridesmaid when a cousin married and I remembered how heavy the bouquets made up of large chrysanthemums had been. Because of this, I decided to have small sprays of rosebuds and freesias for flowers. Sadly, Arthur's father and stepmother did not come as they thought it would be too difficult to travel from Burnley.

After the ceremony and reception, we went to an old friend of the family so I could change into a dress and coat I'd chosen to wear after the wedding. I had known Phyllis all my life but being over eighty she was unable to come to the service, which was a disappointment for her. To make up for this, I delighted her by taking my flowers to give to her. It was good to give something back for I remembered when I was young, Phyllis, although very poor, often brought small gifts to us.

After saying goodbye to Phyllis, Arthur and I caught a train to

London where we stayed for a few days at a hotel to enjoy seeing some of the London sights and a show together.

In the middle of the following week, we returned to Tenby where Arthur had rented a flat for us. As it was a holiday apartment, we were only allowed to stay there until just before Easter but this was several weeks away.

The sitting room was quite large and because of this, difficult to keep warm in winter. For this reason, we converted a smaller room which was easier to keep warm and where we could sit in the dark evenings. As yet, I had not changed my banking arrangements which were with the bank recommended by the army. Now we were short of money and payday was two days away.

The following morning, Arthur went to work and after I had tidied the flat, I wondered what we should have for our evening meal. Before going out, I wrote to the bank arranging to transfer my account. Then just as I was leaving the flat, the post arrived with a letter from my mother enclosing a ten-shilling note. This, she wrote, was from her neighbour to be sent to me as a wedding present. At that time, a ten shilling note was wealth, especially to someone having only a few pence. This ended any problems about what we should eat that evening as I went to the shops. We would be able to have something a little more appetising than vegetable soup.

While I had lived at home when I was younger, my mother had never allowed me to do any cooking so in this respect, I was a complete novice. This might have been a problem but having been instructed in the rudiments of cookery while at school, I had some knowledge. An important item in my luggage was a small instruction book about plain cooking which was to prove really useful. Aided by this and with the knowledge remembered from my schooldays, I was able to prepare our evening meals although at first I had difficulty in timing meat and vegetables so that all were ready together.

Being the only girl in the family, I had been expected to do some of the housework and I had resented having to do things from which my brothers were excused. This was one reason I had disliked housework and tried to avoid it whenever possible. Probably this is why my father had decided I would not make anyone a very good wife. However, looking after my own home, even though temporary was different and in the early years of nurse training, I learned how things should be done.

It was pleasant living in Tenby, even for the short time we were there. Although early in the year, the weather was pleasant and sunny. I spent some time during the afternoons wandering along the beach. This almost ended in disaster for one day, as I walked among the rocks enjoying the sunshine I did not notice the tide had suddenly come in at a great rate. It looked as if I might be cut off from the shore, which seemed rather far away. Slipping off my shoes, I was able to paddle through the water to higher ground.

Weekends were spent together in pleasant walks around the town and the surrounding area, which we both enjoyed during the time we spent there.

MORE CHANGES

The lease of the flat would be at an end just before the Easter holiday began so we would need to look for somewhere else to live. This would not be easy in and around Tenby at holiday time and we would be homeless. Then a few weeks before Easter, Arthur learned he was to be sent on a course at the School of Electronic Engineering in Arborfield near Reading.

Surely, we thought, it would be easier to find somewhere to live in Reading as we packed our belongings into my army tin trunk, which without all my nursing uniform was proving very useful. We were optimistic about this move although we knew nothing about Reading or whether we would find a place to rent. As a last resort, we might have to stay a few nights in a hotel but this would soon deplete our resources.

Although still early in the year, it was quite hot the afternoon we arrived in Reading and leaving most of our luggage at the railway station, started to visit Estate Agents to see what was on offer. We were disillusioned to find there were few places to let except those that were far too expensive. Then at one office, seeing our disappointed faces, the woman assistant there said, "Why don't you go to the end of the King's Road; there is a Newsagent there who has notices in his window about places to let."

"How do we get there?"

"You can get a bus just along the road here."

We thanked her, left to find the bus stop, and soon were on our way past Huntley and Palmers' biscuit factory, then a little further on we alighted close to the Newsagents she had recommended.

We looked eagerly at the advertisements and among the notices saw one advertising a flatlet on the King's Road which we discovered, was quite close by. We walked back along the road towards the town to look for it.

"It must be here," I said looking over a gate into a front garden where a woman was tidying up the flowerbeds.

We walked through the gate and asked, "We have just seen a notice in the newsagent up the road about a flat. Is it still vacant?"

"Yes." She looked at us and scrambled to her feet. "Do you want to see it?"

"Yes please."

"I'm Mrs. Lane. Come in." she said, leading us into the hall. "Wait while I wash my hands," she said disappearing briefly.

Returning, she said, "It's on the top floor."

We followed her up two flights of stairs to the room which took half the top floor space. As by that time we were tired and hungry we were glad to come to arrangements about the rent which was reasonable. The room was pleasant and even if we looked further it was doubtful whether we would find anywhere as suitable. Another reason in its favour was that it was on the bus route into town.

Although the room was not large, it held two single beds, one each side of the window, with a washbasin between. There was a small cooker, cupboards, a wardrobe and a small settee. By no means luxurious but it would suit us and be warm and comfortable.

"You have use of the bathroom on the floor below," Mrs. Lane told us, "but you will have to come to arrangements about baths with the other tenants."

After collecting our luggage from the station, we soon settled in as we did not have many belongings. Arthur had previously lived in Barracks and living in one room was not new to me so living here would be no hardship to either of us. With the basic facilities provided, we would be able to live quite well.

The other tenants, five in all, were generally out at work during the day so we rarely met. In the room opposite ours was a young man who we saw occasionally on our way in and out. Downstairs, one flat was occupied by a mother and her daughter and the other by a woman whose main topic of conversation was Virginia Water.

Once Arthur started at the School in Arborfield, there was little to do during the day; there were no vacancies at the local hospital so I looked for some other work. Scanning the situations vacant in the local newspaper, I noticed that part time workers were needed at Huntley and Palmers. The factory was not far away and I decided to apply. The work consisted of packing biscuits each morning from eight until one. These hours were convenient and any extra money would prove to be useful. A few days later I joined a number of other women to be issued with a white overall and turban. After some initial training we joined the other workers on a production line. The work was not hard but at that time, corrugated paper was used to separate the different kinds of biscuits in the tins and boxes. The edges of this paper could be sharp, making it too easy to cut one's fingers when packing the biscuits. Naturally, there would be trouble if fingers bled onto the biscuits and it meant that our fingers could be covered with plasters.

The other workers at the factory were pleasant and happy to show me what needed to be done in the processes involved. The work was not difficult and by the end of each morning, the walk back to the flat was pleasant.

Many years before, a member of the Huntley family had said in his Will that all workers should be given a pound bag of broken biscuits every Thursday. So in addition to our pay packets, we collected these biscuits. Most were plain but sometimes there were a few sweet ones which we could eat with our evening drink. In one of our walks, we had discovered the River Kennet so any biscuits which were too broken and crumbly were fed to the ducks and swans.

Towards the end of his course, Arthur learned he was to be posted to Germany to join the REME Workshop attached to the Twelfth Regiment Royal Artillery. As yet, he was not eligible for an Army Quarter so would need to find somewhere for us to live once he arrived at the camp. Meantime I would have to stay in England but not wishing to stay alone in Reading or with my parents, I had an idea.

"I think I'll write to the Matron at Selly Oak, explain the situation and see if she can offer me a temporary post for three or four months."

That afternoon, I wrote to Miss Brown at Selly Oak to ask if she had any short-term vacancies and soon a letter came back offering me a post as Night Sister which seemed ideal.

Now that was settled, and a few days before Arthur was due in Germany, I caught a train to Birmingham. We said goodbye at the railway station, hoping that this would not be for long. Being optimistic, I looked forward to seeing my training school again for now it was six years since I left. Things would be quite different for having left as a Staff Nurse; I would be in a different position as one of the Night Sisters.

BACK TO THE BEGINNING

Arriving at the Night Sisters' office, the following evening, after knocking, I walked in. The sister sitting at the desk inside looked up and then as she recognised me beamed broadly.

"Well," she said, "I wondered about the new sister as I did not recognise the name. Welcome back to us."

"How nice to see you again," I said, surprised to see a familiar face. Staff Nurse Cox was now one of the Night Sisters. It was good to see her for I had learned so much from her as a student on Ward D3. Her greeting allayed my anxieties and I knew my time back at Selly Oak would be fine.

Being Night Sister in a busy General Hospital was completely different to night duty in a Military Hospital. Three years in the army had prepared me for change, so it did not take long to settle in and adapt to the routine. There was a lot to learn about the patients on the wards allocated to me. Getting to know the nurses and help with their training kept me busy for then I did not have time to feel sorry for myself and wish I were with Arthur in Germany.

Knowing the hospital, it was not difficult to find the way round the wards although at first it was strange to be back where my nursing career had started.

In this new status as Sister, a cup of tea was brought to me each evening; this was quite enjoyable, while getting ready for duty. This was not to last long for after the fourth week, I had a sudden feeling of nausea as I drank it. Probably due to being unused to getting up in the evening. I thought but as this continued for several nights, I had to refuse any more tea, having water instead. I thought nothing of this until one night, in the dining room, I looked at my meal and felt nauseated. In sudden awareness, I realised there was only one thing wrong and it was that I was pregnant. Strangely, after this, I had no more sickness.

I made an appointment to see the gynaecologist, the same consultant who had been parodied in a Christmas concert. He confirmed my pregnancy and life continued normally. A few mornings later, I went to the Pathological laboratory for routine blood tests.

The young technician looked at me and said, " would you like someone more experienced to do this?"

I smiled at him and said, "Don't worry, I'm just a patient at the moment."

Nevertheless he had difficulty in obtaining enough blood and apologised profusely for having several tries to get any at all.

Not long after this, a letter arrived from Arthur in which he said he would be able to get a lift with friends who were going to the Motor Show in London the following weekend. Would I be able to join him and if so, could I find somewhere to stay? Luckily my nights off coincided with this trip and I wrote back to organise where we would meet. Meantime, looking for accommodation, I was able to book a room in a small hotel not far from the city centre.

It was good to see each other again and spend time together. We were amused at the hotel that seemed to have rather an odd clientele. Hearing snatches of words as we passed them in the foyer, we speculated as to whether they were East European spies. This did not deter our enjoyment of this weekend during which we visited the Motor Show. It was there we saw a small Renault car we thought might suit us for although quite basic, the price was reasonable. All too soon, the time passed and we said our reluctant goodbyes although Arthur was sure it would not be long before we had a place to live in Germany.

On my other nights off, I was able to visit some of the places I knew in and near Birmingham. It was also good to visit friends and relations still living there.

Another month passed and I was beginning to feel quite tired on night duty. Perhaps it might be better to transfer to day duty. When I went to see Matron to ask about this, she said there were no vacancies.

Reluctantly, I then gave notice to leave at the end of the following month, which would give a little over the three months we had planned previously. I then arranged to stay with my parents until an Army Quarter became available. Then, during my final week, a letter arrived from Arthur to say we had a place to live. A day or two later an official letter confirmed this with documentation about transport to Germany. It also gave particulars about moving to Delmenhorst in the north of Germany. This meant I would be with my parents just over a week before moving. There was quite a lot to get ready so it was a busy time and the days flew by.

My mother was pleased to see me again and surprised me when she said, "We shall soon have some new babies in the family."

"Oh?" I said, wondering if she had guessed about me.

"Gordon and David's wives are both pregnant and expecting their babies within a month of each other, next January and February."

"Well," I said, "You can make it three for my baby is due in April."

It was a surprise to her and she could hardly wait to tell her friends and start knitting for yet another grandchild hoping that at least one of them would be a boy as she already had two granddaughters.

The plane to take me to Hanover left from Manchester. My parents insisted on saying goodbye at the airport but after they left, due to a thick fog, planes were not allowed to take off. All the passengers were taken to Buxton to stay overnight in a hotel and as by morning the fog had cleared, the plane took off safely.

GERMANY

Arriving in Germany, I was directed to the railway station or Bahnhof to get the train to Delmenhorst. It seemed strange to hear a different language, all notices and directions were in German making it difficult for a foreigner. My phrase book seemed of little use where everyone was in a hurry. First, I had to cope with luggage and find the train to Delmenhorst, then eventually, a seat on the train. Even then, I was full of doubt wondering if this actually was the right train. There were strange names at the stations where we stopped, each as unfamiliar as the last. It was a relief when, in the late afternoon, I heard the name Delmenhorst shouted and saw Arthur waiting on the platform, and knew I was home.

The house we had been allocated was in a small terrace where other army families lived. Number twenty-eight Rubenstrasse was a pleasant red brick building which seemed to welcome me. There was a reasonably sized main room that looked over a garden which on that first evening was too dark to see properly. The kitchen was at the front of the house, overlooking the street. I liked this for when working in the kitchen, it was good to see people passing and give them a friendly wave.

Upstairs were two bedrooms and a bathroom and above these, an attic with pull down steps. Later, I found this ideal to hang washing when the weather was bad; although it was cold, the clothes dried slowly. Below the kitchen was a cellar that held a boiler, sink and a rather old-fashioned mangle. Next to this in a separate cellar, coke for the boiler was stored and delivered by means of an opening outside.

It did not take us long to make this place comfortable and as Arthur had already been 'marched in'; he had signed all the necessary paperwork. On the wards in the army, we had a regular inventory to make sure nothing was missing, In Army married quarters, something similar took place on arrival and departure.

Every detail was inspected, every sheet, pillow and utensil was checked and the edges of tables and worktops scanned for cigarette burns. This was repeated when a family left and anything missing had to be paid for. I did not find out whether there was a penalty for the cigarette burns for as neither of us smoked, there were no extra burns to be counted when we eventually moved.

The next day, Arthur showed me where to find the shops and also the NAAFI, (Navy, Army and Air Force Institutes) where most necessities could be purchased. Later, I found it was often better to use the local shops for many of my purchases as some were cheaper and we both liked to experiment with local food. Surprisingly, the language did not cause difficulties as the British Army had been stationed there for several years. Almost everyone spoke some English and when I went into a shop, phrasebook in hand to make a purchase, there was always someone eager to help who would come to say they spoke English.

Delmenhorst was a friendly town with a small park in which to relax and watch the people passing by. It was especially enjoyable to go to the market for the stallholders were all helpful and ready to show their produce. They were always ready to give customers a piece of cheese or salami to try before buying. It was not long before I felt at ease with the people I met and able to talk to them with the aid of my phrase book and the words I learned.

It was pleasing to see how much the local people liked children.

One of my neighbours said her two small children never came home from the market without apples and oranges given to them by the generous stallholders. Later, when my pregnancy became more noticeable the stallholders always asked how I was and how long before the baby came.

Next door to us lived a friendly Indian woman married to a Bombardier. In the Artillery, the privates are called gunners and corporals are known as Lance Bombardiers and Bombardiers. Kitty showed me how to cook rice in the Indian way so that it was never sticky.

"First you measure how much rice you want, a cupful should be enough for two." She demonstrated by pouring the rice into a cup.

"Then you must wash the rice well to take away the starch," she continued as she put the rice into a sieve and poured water copiously through it.

"Put into a saucepan, add salt and water just over half an inch higher. Then you put it on a very low heat and leave it until cooked."

This was a good method and even an amateur cook like me was able to cook rice successfully.

Once a week, a wives club was held and all who could went there; it was a good place to get to know and make friends with other wives. Another thriving part of army life was the thrift club where outgrown clothing could be taken to be sold. This was very popular and especially useful for those with children.

My priority was to go to the Antenatal clinic and arrange for where our baby would be born. The nearest Army Hospital was in Hanover but the clinic was held in a small town about midway between Delmenhorst and Hanover. When given an appointment, army transport was available for the journey. When I arrived, a German nurse took my particulars, weighed me, took my blood pressure before I went in to see the doctor.

This was a great surprise for as he looked up to greet me, we recognised each other immediately for it was Major Collins from Woolwich. I think he was as surprised to see me as I was to see him. He pointed to the extra pip on his tunic and proudly said, "I've been promoted to Lieutenant Colonel since we last met."

"Congratulations. You deserve it." I said.

"So you are now doing part three?" he said.

During training to become a midwife it was a standard joke among us about who would be the first to go on to Part Three Training which of course was having our own baby and learning about it first hand.

Before this I had worked out the expected date the baby was due as being April eleventh but he decided it would be the fourteenth.

It would soon be Christmas and preparations were being made for the holiday. My friend, Joan was invited to stay with us for a few days and arrived a few days before the holiday, minus luggage for this had gone astray. Luckily, Joan and I were of similar height and build so she was able to borrow some of my clothes until her own arrived not long afterwards.

The city of Bremen was quite near, so we decided to go there to see the Christmas Decorations. Each shop was beautifully decorated with Christmas scenes depicted in the windows. We enjoyed wandering around the older part of the town which has many medieval buildings. Despite our warmest clothing, we were cold and our fingers and toes were becoming numb. Then as we turned a corner, we saw the statue of 'The Town Musicians', which I remembered from reading some of the Grimm's fairy tales. The story is about a donkey making its way to Bremen to become a musician; on its journey, it meets a dog, a cat and a cockerel who travel with him. They frighten some robbers by all making as much 'music' as they can. Although the musicians never actually reached Bremen. the statue, in bronze was erected in the town.

After the holiday, the weather became extremely cold and snow began to fall transforming the street. This snow was powdery and like sand to sweep away, not melting and forming a wet slush as at home. Some of the German housewives who passed the house pulled a sledge along behind them with their shopping or a small child sitting and smiling proudly. On my next visit to the clinic, the weather was bitterly cold and because there were several of us, we travelled in a minibus that had little or no heating. We sat huddled together to try and keep warm but it was good to be home and in a warm house once more.

The Army Medical Officer had discovered I was a midwife and one day sent to ask if I would visit an officer's wife who was threatening to miscarry. Unfortunately, when I arrived, it was too late as despite sedatives her very early pregnancy had ended. There was little for me to do other than check everything was complete and to make sure that she had all she needed and reassure her about any future pregnancy.

At the end of March, my mother wrote to tell me that she now had two grandsons, born in February and March and she was waiting to see if she would have another.

Time passed quickly until admission to the British Military Hospital in Hanover. I had persuaded the obstetrician to admit me only three days before my expected date, instead of a week as he usually did. This meant I was there only a few days before James was born on the fourteenth of April. So now my mother had three grandsons.

The following week it was the Easter holiday and I was allowed home on Easter Monday. After childbirth at that time, mothers were kept in hospital for at least ten days which in many ways was good, allowing the mothers to be helped with breast-feeding and care of stitches where necessary. Although in my work I had been accustomed to this routine, I could sympathise with those mothers who were impatient to leave.

Arriving home, I had to establish a new routine for now there were three of us. It was quite a change and fortunately, James was quite a good baby. All the neighbours wanted to see him and the local people who passed regularly on their way to the nearby allotments stopped to see and ask about him.

Opposite our house, a Bombardier and his wife Rose lived. After years of believing she was unable to have children, to her delight, she became pregnant. It was even more surprising to learn she was having twins and time was spent discussing how she would cope. In fact she managed her little girls very well when they arrived safely a few months later.

At that time, the men were often away at Practice camps for two weeks in the north of the country where they could fire the guns safely. In addition to this there was another exercise called 'Quick Train' where the men had to be ready and away in about five minutes from receiving the call. It was amazing to see how quickly they could be prepared with full kit even in the early hours of the morning.

During these army exercises, most of the wives, apart from those whose husbands were working in the camp on clerical duties, were alone. The wives' club still met weekly and baby-sitting was organised so that most were able to go even when the men were away.

Having seen a car within our price range in London, the previous year we decided to buy a Renault Four, which would be a means of taking us away for the occasional break. If it was possible to collect the car from the factory in France the price was even better. The difficulty was that Arthur had not yet passed his driving test so could not collect the car on his own and I was not sufficiently experienced to drive a strange car. We asked Jim, a friend from Gibraltar, to help and when he agreed, Arthur met him in France and Jim drove the car to Delmenhorst, staying with us for a few days afterwards. Not long after this Arthur passed his driving test and we could spend several weekends away.

As a new mother, I was visited by the SAFFA Sister (Soldier, Sailor and Air Force Association) and we soon became friends. Kate was the equivalent of a Health Visitor in the forces and often came to visit us when off duty.

James was a happy baby and made many friends around us; Usha, a clerical worker at the Camp loved to come and visit. On several occasions, she took him to visit her parents who were delighted, as he had fair hair and blue eyes of the Aryan type which many German people loved.

Once a week, an elderly German man came to us with eggs for sale, heralding his approach with a shout of 'egg man.' Everyone we met was very friendly and it was difficult to believe that not long before we had been at war with Germany. Perhaps we had thought our lives were hard during those years but it seemed that most of the German population had a much harder time.

One weekend we visited the town of Hamelin, famous for the Pied Piper who charmed away the rats that infested the town. When the citizens refused to pay him, he then played his pipe and all the children followed him and were never seen again.

Another weekend, as we drove through the countryside we saw a signpost pointing to Belsen and followed this road leading to the former concentration camp. It was lonely with very little traffic when we arrived at the camp and parked the car. It seemed to me that a sense of sadness pervaded the air inside as we walked round and saw the huge burial mounds. About fifty thousand people died there during the war.

Returning to the car, I wondered if perhaps the reason that few people seemed to know what was going on was because of the isolation of the camp and perhaps those who did know were too afraid to say anything.

James was growing fast and now delighted in exploring around the house and trying to take his first steps. When he reached his first birthday we spent a few days touring through the north of Germany. Soon we would leave Germany for England and the next posting which would be to the Far East.

As the Regiment had been stationed in Delmenhorst for some years and had a good relationship there, they were given the freedom the town. A parade was held with speeches made by the Mayor and Colonel and the Regiment left with the good wishes of the townspeople.

ANOTHER MOVE

THE FAR EAST

Living in a caravan for one or two weeks on holiday can be enjoyable if the weather is good but living in one for three or four months as a temporary home in England is completely different.

Although we had been married for over two years, we had already lived in three different types of home and this would be the fourth. To move a whole regiment and find the men and families somewhere to live whilst waiting to be transported to the Far East would be no easy matter. The solution was to put them all into temporary accommodation on a disused barrack square.

Our new home was in Hampshire at Barton Stacey near Andover.

Life in Germany had been agreeable and when we heard about the move, we decided to drive back to England in easy stages by car.

Our journey, in the month of May was pleasant and rather than face the channel crossing by sea, we took the air ferry which although rather bumpy, at least was quick.

Arriving in Barton Stacey, we were allocated a small caravan. It was quite a feat, stowing our entire luggage away to leave the cramped space as free as possible. At night, a large pull down bed occupied most of the space and a smaller one was made as safe as possible for James.

When we arrived, the toilets were a distance away but later, stand pipes and wooden structures holding toilets were put up next to each caravan. This made life easier especially for those with children, during the three months we were there.

Luckily, for most of the time, the weather was generally fine; James and I were able to take walks around the area enjoying the wild life. Probably his love of wild life and birds dated from that time. We made friends with other families and were able to take trips into Andover together. One of them was Jean and as there was little housework to do, we spent most of our time exploring the area.

Meantime, arrangements were being made for travel to Malaysia to the small town of Tampin. Nearly everyone would be allocated an Army quarter but we were low on the priority list. With a toddler to care for, there was no question of working so my next move with James was to my parents for a while.

James and I settled in happily and were able to visit my brother David, his wife Janet and their son Nigel, who were living near Derby. James enjoyed walks round the village and being in the garden with his grandfather.

Not long after this, Arthur was promoted to Sergeant and when the Medical Officer realised how far the camp in Tampin was from an Army Hospital, he realised a Midwife was needed urgently. Because of this and knowing of my background, it was not long before a house was available and arrangements made for travel.

Just before we were due to fly to Malaysia, David and Janet's second son, Roger was born so my mother now had four grandsons.

The first part of our journey was by train from the little station near my parent's house. James, now eighteen months old enjoyed watching the fields and houses flashing by. Although the journey was long, James did not mind, as he was interested in everything going on around him. There were stops in Istanbul and Bombay where we were allowed to leave the plane while it refuelled. We were both unprepared for the overpowering heat as we stepped off the plane in Bombay. James quickly pulled off the knitted sweater he had needed in England but found too stifling in the heat. He insisted on walking around the airport building where he saw a woman in a sari and was intrigued by her dark face. When at last we returned to our seat, his sweater was missing. Someone had taken it but if that person was returning to England, it would be found useful and as before long it would be too small for James, I did not mind. Tiring of watching the people around us, James at last settled down and slept until we were called to re-embark on our plane.

Our next stop was Colombo and then it was not long before arriving in Singapore but before this, we flew into a storm which jolted the plane severely and made me feel quite sick. Thankfully, James fell asleep through this, waking as soon as the plane touched down. He was alert immediately and wanting to be the first to leave the plane. It was difficult to restrain him while trying to gather our possessions together.

Arthur was waiting for us with the car, which by then had been shipped out. He had organised a rattan car seat for James which he enjoyed as this enabled him to look out of the car windows at the passing scenery.

By the time we arrived in Tampin, it was dark and we were tired and ready to sleep. The following morning we looked round the bungalow that would be our home for the next two and a half years. Three airy bedrooms looked onto the garden which extended around the building. There was an open plan living and dining area with a large kitchen. Leading from this was the amah's room and beyond this, a washroom where there was a huge sink and an Asian style toilet.

A wide monsoon drain ran through the garden which I felt would be a hazard for James. We remedied this by having a small wooden bridge built, over which he loved to walk.

Most days the temperature was very high and humid but ceiling fans in the rooms kept us cool. At night, mosquito nets were used over the beds for there was the danger of Malaria although we all took a daily dose of Paludrine to prevent this.

The gate was reached by a steep drive that opened on to a road on the hillside. On one side a steep bend in the road led upward, on the other, a similar bend led downward. Across the road scrubland led to the jungle clad slopes of Tampin Hill. A strong chain and clasp, easy for an adult to remove but too high for a child was obtained to make sure James would be safe.

Our Amah, Mary arrived a few days later and was eager to start work.

"I come from Ceylon and my mother was a Dutch Burgher," she told us.

I had no idea what this meant but found out that when the Dutch living in Ceylon had children by the native population, these children were known as Dutch Burghers. Mary was very black, even more so than her husband who was a Tamil from Ceylon.

"One of my boys will help in the garden," she said and we were pleased to employ him.

In Malaysia, the local people keep all English holidays, also Chinese New Year, Muslim and Indian holidays. We had been in Malaysia just one week when the Festival of Lights or Deepavali was celebrated so Mary was off that day. I did not expect this to cause any problems and having just finished breakfast, Arthur left for work at the army camp. A sudden screeching of brakes made me look out. An army ambulance had stopped on the hill outside and an orderly jumped out and came to the door.

"There's a woman in labour in the ambulance. Can you go with her to the hospital?" he asked.

"I must look at her first," was my reply. "Please look after my son while I do."

It was easy to see by looking at her that she was almost into the second stage of labour. Her husband, dressed in jungle green sat beside her looking tired and worried for he had been on duty all night.

Returning to the house I told the orderly, "I'm afraid she will be having this baby very soon. Have you any equipment, sterile towels, forceps, scissors?"

He looked at me with a blank expression and said, "No!"

"Well, get back to camp as quickly as you can and ask the Medical Officer for some things, please. He should know what you need."

He disappeared down the road and with little time to waste, I called to my neighbour in the next bungalow and asked if she could look after James.

I then said to the husband, "Encourage your wife to take deep breaths when she gets a pain, I'll be back as quickly as I can."

I ran into the bungalow and grabbed scissors, string and a basin which I hastily boiled on the stove. Taking some clean towels from a drawer, I drained the water away and ran out again.

"I'm sorry I had to leave you but I needed just a few things," I said and looked at the patient. "It won't be long now for I can see your baby's head."

Soon the infant was crying lustily as I tied his cord in two places and separated it. Wrapping him in a towel, I handed him to his mother.

"He looks a fine healthy baby," I told her, "the MO will check him over later but he looks fine."

By this time, the afterbirth was showing signs of separation and was soon delivered and looked complete.

All this time, the woman's husband had been sitting in a corner of the ambulance, hardly daring to move so I thanked him for being so patient and congratulated him on his new son.

There was a noise outside and the orderly and MO appeared.

"Sorry about this," the MO said, "but I was not expecting this kind of emergency. I'm afraid we haven't got any of the things we should have."

"Will I still have to go to hospital?" the patient asked.

"I'm afraid so," he answered, "but we'll let you rest first.

"Did you bring ergometrine?" I asked.

He produced a syringe and an ampoule which I drew up and gave to the patient.

"Can you go with her to Kin-Rara?" he asked.

"If my neighbour will be kind enough to look after my little boy," I replied.

At this point, I did not know where the hospital was but later was told it was in Kuala Lumpur about seventy miles away.

Vallie, my neighbour was quite happy to keep James with her until Arthur finished work and as they were already becoming friends, I went to change my dress and get ready for the journey. It was very hot and my patient was flushed and perspiring. It was difficult to keep her cool at the same time making sure she was not losing any blood after the baby's unexpectedly quick arrival.

Later, at the hospital, I took mother and child to the maternity ward and informed the sisters there about her.

"Will you stay for lunch?" they asked and as by this time, I was hungry and glad to consent. The journey back was uneventful and I found that James had spent an interesting day and was now fast asleep.

The following day I reported to the MO to let him know that the patient had been admitted and everything was all right. He asked me if I would be willing to be ready to take other patients to hospital if necessary.

"I will be happy to do so," I said, "providing I have some basic equipment."

"I'll get that sorted out as soon as possible, but before we can take you on officially, you will need to have the approval of the Director of Army Medical Services and I'll arrange this as soon as possible."

ANOTHER INTERVIEW

An interview with the man in charge of army medical services in the Far East took place a few days later. This was different from the formal interviews prior to Nurse Training.

Walking into the Medical Centre office we looked at each other and he said, "Haven't we met before?" .

With a smile, I answered, "Yes, I was one of the sisters in Gibraltar."

After discussing the experience gained as a midwife in the army, he said, "I'm sure you will get along with everyone if you will agree to work here."

"Yes, I'm looking forward to it," I said.

It was decided that I should work in the Medical Centre in the mornings helping with the routine and injections and be on call for anyone nearly due to have their baby. Mary, the Amah was happy to look after James in the mornings until, when he was two years old, there was a place available in the little nursery run by some of the Army wives. This he enjoyed very much and quickly made friends with the other children.

Before then, I was called to a house on the estate where a woman was in labour. The MO had examined her and decided it was too late to send her to hospital. With the help of one of the medical orderlies the equipment was set up ready for the delivery. The MO wanted to deliver the baby and I was ready to assist. There was some delay and on examining the patient, I realised that this baby was presenting by the face. Fortunately, as in my third delivery on district, it was a third pregnancy and in the right position. With a little help, the baby was delivered and as in the previous face presentation, everything went well.

Having made the mother comfortable, we left with a promise to see her the following day. The MO would have liked to keep her at home but having checked with the obstetrician at the hospital, was told she must be transferred. The following day, I went with her to the Kin-Rara Hospital but this time the journey was not a problem.

Many of the women did not give the correct due dates about their babies date of delivery. This was because if the pregnancy was past a certain number of weeks, they were not allowed to fly and would have to wait until several weeks after the birth before joining their husbands. No one wanted to wait so long which meant many were much further on in pregnancy than they admitted.

Every morning in the Medical Centre, I assisted with medical examinations and immunisations for the troops. The men often needed boosters or extra immunisations, and if sent to Aden needed cover for Yellow Fever.

There were two Medical Orderlies who organised the necessary paper work and kept the troops in order. It was surprising to see how sometimes strong, fit men reacted to a small prick in the arm. They could face all sorts of hardships in the jungle, being bitten by insects or leeches but reacted nervously when seeing a hypodermic needle.

Each Monday afternoon, a Sister from SAFFA (Soldiers, Sailors and Air Force Institutions) visited the camp. She was responsible for the health of children and any pregnant wives. As she lived thirty miles away in Seremban, most of this care was left to me. Together, we gave immunisations to the babies and small children and examined the pregnant women.

Possibly, because of the heat and humidity in the tropics, wounds did not heal well and needed extra care with dressings; this was another part of my duties. One of the wives had a gall bladder operation which took a while to heal and needed dressing every day but eventually healed satisfactorily.

During our stay in Malaysia, a new hospital was built at Terendak near Malacca and when this was opened, the journey was only twenty-five miles. The hospital and equipment at Kin-Rara was transfered to the Malaysians.

Early one morning, I was called out to Lynton Court, another Army quarter where I found the woman had already given birth, a BBA (born before arrival of medical help) as these were called. The birth had been straightforward and I delivered the afterbirth without any problems. It was her sixth pregnancy and later, she was transferred to hospital with her baby.

Some afternoons we would wander around the town of Tampin or perhaps go further to the larger town of Seremban. The shops and their owners were interesting; some were Chinese, others Indian but there were very few Malay shops.

At a Chinese shop, we bought some cheap but sturdy Rattan furniture. Most Chinese shops had a variety of different occupations within one family. The head of the family might sell and mend watches, his son make rattan furniture, his wife often sold material and the daughters were dressmakers. No one was idle for apparently they were all saving to keep other members of the family at universities as far apart as England, Australia and America. We noticed a round table for family meals at the back of most Chinese shops. Being round, no-one sitting there could think themselves more important than anyone else.

One very hot, humid day, the air was still without any breeze as I waited at a shop. The owner handed me a piece of carved wood which opened into a little fan, which was ideal to cool the air near my face. I wanted to buy it but he said it was a present and refused payment.

Our life seemed pleasant but this did not last for there were problems in Indonesia and one battery of the regiment was sent to Sarawak to deal with any trouble. Those REME Personnel who were attached to the battery had to go with them to keep the equipment in working order. This meant that Arthur had to go too as he was in charge of the necessary electronic apparatus.

Whilst Arthur was away, I asked the amah to stay at night to be there to look after James should I be called out to take someone to hospital. This she agreed to do and early one morning, I was called to take a woman in the early stages of labour to the hospital in Malacca. Army ambulances were very uncomfortable; anyone travelling in them was jolted at each bump in the road. This was not the best treatment for someone in labour and it could be most unpleasant for any patients, more so for those in pain.

Due to the extreme bumpiness of the journey as we were driven through some padi (rice) fields, her labour advanced rapidly. As we were only about half way, it was unlikely she would reach hospital before the baby was born. I asked the driver to stop but then, in the confined space the heat became intolerable. My patient was getting distressed so I asked the driver to open the back doors to allow cooler air into the ambulance.

By now, a crowd of children, seeing something unusual happening, had gathered around.

Mohammed was worried. "What can I do about the children?" he asked.

"Try to keep them away," I said, "Stand with your back to us and keep them from coming too close."

Still looking rather worried, he did so and I was able to open the Delivery Pack with which the ambulances were now equipped.

As I put on some gloves, I talked to my patient, "it will not be long now, just keep taking deep breaths."

Very soon, a healthy boy was delivered and cried loudly, sending a cheer through the crowd of children. As soon as everything was dealt with, we waited for the ambulance to cool down and my patient to rest and recover. On reaching the hospital, having seen she was comfortable, I said goodbye and left. The baby weighed over eight pounds so obviously was not premature.

There were two ambulance drivers at the camp, both Malay; one was called Mohammed bin Abdul whose wife Norma worked in the NAAFI and Abdul bin Mohammed. The "bin" means 'son of'; they were not related to each other but both were pleasant and obliging, which made our journeys less difficult.

Sadly, not long before I left Malaysia, Abdul was diagnosed as having a brain tumour and in spite of treatment, died. A quiet friendly man, he was very much missed by all the Medical staff.

One night, the call came to take someone else to hospital, this time, although the patient was in labour, the journey was uneventful. At about three in the morning, we drove back to Tampin through the rubber plantations. I watched lights flickering among the trees and later found these belonged to rubber tappers. Apparently they were up early each morning to cut the trees so that as the sap began to flow, it was caught in small cups fastened to the tree. Later, as it grew lighter, these could be seen below the cuts on each tree. Later still in the day, after the latex had been collected, the cups were turned onto their sides.

Mohammed's wife Norma had been attending the anti-natal clinic and we were all pleased when their baby arrived. Norma invited me to visit the house where they lived with many members of their extended family. This house was built on stilts, and animals belonging to the family lived in the area underneath.

Steps led up to the front and I was taken into a large room where the new baby was sleeping in a hammock suspended by thick elastic bands of the kind used to keep luggage in place on cars. When someone walked past, a gentle push was given to rock the baby who lay quietly and was obviously contented.

An entirely different Malay house was the one where Mary the amah lived, in what was known as the 'Indian Village'. Although made of wood it was not raised from the ground, which appeared to be bare earth covered with rush matting. The roof was of corrugated iron and in the monsoon, the noise of rain on this roof was deafening.

DIFFERENT EVENTS

One evening, I drove into Tampin to a hairdresser, leaving the car on the main road outside. There were trees on each side and I had forgotten that numerous birds roosted there at night. Going back to the car, it was covered with bird droppings and the windscreen had to be cleaned before driving home. Once there, the car needed to be washed completely but even at night, it was hot and humid and when finished, I was perspiring profusely; having my hair set had been a futile exercise.

Rose, who had lived close to us in Delmenhorst, was now living in the Army Quarters known as Sleepy Valley. Her twins, Barbara and Wendy were lively and active and enjoyed having James as a companion. One day, running round their bungalow, which unlike ours was on stilts, they got a little too boisterous and James slipped and fell. He recovered quickly but complained later that his shoulder hurt but this did not seem to inconvenience him. Two days later, I noticed a small lump on his collarbone and took him to see the MO. A greenstick fracture showed on X-ray and a collar and cuff sling was applied. He did not tolerate this long and as he was running around quite happily, I felt it was unnecessary.

One very hot afternoon, I was having a cup of tea; James, who had just gone into the garden called to me. I went outside to see what he wanted but had a shock when I almost trod on a snake curled on the path. It hissed and darted away towards the car as I called in panic to the amah.

"Mary! Come quickly! A snake!"

In a moment, she was there and I pointed towards the car.

"It went under there."

Quickly Mary found a stick and used it to poke under the car which was even more worrying.

"Do be careful," I cautioned her.

As the snake slipped out, she used the stick to batter it and in moments it lay lifeless on the path. Now it did not seem at all menacing but a small, dark rather pathetic creature.

I went to see if James was all right and make sure there were no other snakes in the area. Meantime, Mary found a jam jar into which she carefully placed the snake. Seeing this, I decided to take the snake to the Medical Centre and find out more about it. One of the school teachers was an expert on snakes and came to look at it. She took the jar and turned it carefully before giving her diagnosis.

"Only a harmless fruit snake," she said.

I thought of my reaction on first seeing the snake; my hair actually stood on end and my scalp prickled. Although living so close to the jungle, snakes were a rarity and the nearest ones I saw were on a neighbour's roof.

There was a variety of interesting wild life in and around the bungalow, not all welcome for it was difficult to prevent them from coming inside the house. Ants were everywhere, minute ones formed lines up and down the walls as they marched about. Everything had to be sealed tightly to keep them away from food. There were small lizards that probably ate some of the ants and also any other edible creatures. These lizards, known as chit-chats due to the noise they made were lively but harmless.

Not so welcome were the cockroaches that were huge, or the occasional centipede or millipede. At night, flying ants were attracted by lights and flew into the house in hundreds through every nook and cranny they could find. They appeared about every three weeks and the only thing to do was to switch off all the lights and go to bed. Sometimes they even managed to get through the mosquito nets. In the morning on the floor there were piles of the wings they had shed but no sign of the ants.

Outside, we often saw a praying mantis, colourful grasshoppers and sometimes tree frogs. We watched soldier ants marching through the garden, often carrying another, much larger creature. In the jungle monkeys called to one another but never came close enough to be seen.

A local Malaysian school was situated just outside the camp gate and each morning and afternoon, I saw the children in their uniforms going in and out.

One of these was an Indian girl who lived on the edge of Tampin town. At the gate of the camp, a young Indian soldier in the Military Police was often on guard and was attracted to her. He decided to find out about her and having done so, visited her parents and asked if he could marry her. Apparently, the parents liked his manner and decided to say yes if she was agreeable but they must wait until she was sixteen.

I first heard of this romance when her husband brought her to the Medical Centre because she was pregnant. The young couple appeared to be very much in love and watched each other with adoring eyes. She was very shy but I soon made friends with her as I explained what she would expect during her pregnancy and labour. When I admired the beautiful silk sari she was wearing, she told me it was her best and yet, only being married for a short time, she had only three of these. Over the months of her pregnancy, I got to know her very well and was invited to her parent's home when the new baby, a boy was 'named', the Hindu equivalent to our christening.

Later, I was invited by this family to the festival of Thiapusum in their temple which was on the edge of Tampin. I asked if I could take my camera and they were happy for me to do so and I was able to obtain several pictures of the ceremony. In this, many of the worshippers do penance and their way of doing this is piercing the body with long sharpened pieces of metal or silver arrowheads. Some of these were pierced through the penitent's cheeks and tongue, others through the tongue in two directions. After this they move, bare footed, in procession carrying baskets suspended above their heads to another Temple about a mile away. This was explained to me as going from the son to the father. At the larger temple all the spikes were removed from their penitent's bodies, cheeks and tongues and in spite of these sharp piercings; I only saw a few smears of blood.

These piercings could also be a way of giving thanks to the deity for the answer to prayers or for something good that had happened such as recovering from an illness during the preceding months. At this ceremony, a small boy who was probably only about six years of age carried a large basket on his head, an offering of thanks for his mother who had recovered from a severe illness. In his case, no piercing was allowed and someone stayed close to make sure he could manage this task which must have been quite an ordeal for a small boy.

MORE HAPPENINGS

Once the Regiment and their families were established in their quarters, there was not such a problem with women being in advanced labour before calling for assistance. As a rule, women were admitted to hospital about a week before their due date but I think many of them tended to add a week or two to the expected date to avoid having to go into hospital.

This is probably why early one morning I was called to a woman who had said her baby was not due for another ten days or so. When I saw her, she appeared to be only in very early labour and would most likely get to hospital in time. We must only have been a short distance on the way to hospital when her labour became more pronounced. Asking the driver to stop, I examined her and realised delivery was imminent. This time we were near a palm oil plantation and the birth proceeded without delay. In most cases when babies decide to arrive so quickly, usually all goes well. In this case, the baby girl weighed seven pounds eleven ounces.

Having given the mother time to rest and made sure that all was well we went on our way to the hospital. When mother and baby had been admitted, I was able to return home to shower and change before going to camp for my normal duties.

About this time, there was trouble in the area; it was believed that communists and insurgents had infiltrated the area and were hiding in the jungle. It was decided that an armed guard should travel with the ambulance when anyone went to hospital. Also, in the area around Tampin, there were problems with some of the local people who were angry because a child had been hurt by an army lorry. Some of the people were antagonistic towards any army vehicle, which of course included ambulances. Luckily, this problem did not last too long and everything returned to normal once more.

Part of my work was to travel to hospital with any mother who was likely to have complications such as high blood pressure or twins. Some of the women were very nervous and worried especially if the ambulance stopped for any reason. If the woman's husband was available, he would go with her but a nurse was also needed to travel with some of the women who were to be admitted. Generally, though everything went well and no shots were fired.

Whilst Arthur was away in Kuching, my friend Breda who was now stationed in Ipoh, came to stay. It was good to talk together about our experiences in Gibraltar. James liked her immediately and followed her around, eager to show his toys. I had bought him a small tricycle for his third birthday and he loved to ride up to the gate and freewheel down the drive, a game of which he never seemed to tire.

Breda spent an enjoyable week in Tampin also visiting Malacca and Seremban, the nearest towns. As full of fun as ever, Breda decided we should ask the amah to make us a curry on our last night together. Although Mary, the amah assured us it was not as hot as she usually made, to us, it seemed excessively hot and we drank copious amounts of water in an attempt to cool our mouths. As the train to Ipoh left about three in the morning, we did not get much sleep that night. Having driven Breda to Tampin station and said a reluctant goodbye, I arrived home to find a thank you note. This said, 'thank you for a lovely stay and thank Mary for the curry which has left me scorched all through!'

Not long after this, the remaining battery of the regiment went to

Kuching in Sarawak and the first battery was expected to return to Tampin but no one knew when this would be.

About three one morning, I was wakened by tapping on my window and a quiet voice asked, "May I come in?"

It was Arthur who had returned from Kuching and travelled from Singapore on the early morning train. It was wonderful to see him again as I let him in and although we tried to make as little noise as possible, James woke up and called out. As soon as he saw Arthur standing by the door, his face lit up and he laughed with joy. It was difficult for him to go back to bed but eventually he did.

Having the men back, everyone thought that life would return to normal for a while. This did not happen as then there was trouble in Singapore and part of the remaining battery were sent there for two weeks alternating fortnightly. Our lives revolved around these alternate weeks and being busy, I found the two weeks when Arthur was away seemed to speed by. Of course, the two weeks he was in camp also passed quickly but it was good to look forward to these times.

Not long after this, Mary left us and Wong, a Chinese amah, came to us, a pleasant woman who we all liked.

James and I loved to go to the market in Tampin where different vegetables and fruit were sold and he liked to try them all. In a shop near the market, we often watched a man making some kind of pastry, which he pummelled and flapped onto a board until it was quite thin, he then kneaded into a ball and started over again.

Another afternoon, we noticed a crowd gathering and heard notes of music and went to see what was happening. The people let us through to see a snake charmer who opened his basket. A large cobra, head swaying from side to side appeared and the crowd jumped back for it was a scary moment.

We had heard about a famous fruit called the durian and how it had a wonderful taste but a disgusting smell so we decided to try this. Arriving home with one, we asked Wong to take off the thick outer skin so we could taste the flesh. When she did so, the smell was so bad, we told her she could have it if she took it home as soon as possible. This she did but even as she rode down the hill on her bicycle, the smell drifted back to us.

These fruits are not allowed in hotels because of the smell but the people of Malaysia love them. They are quite expensive but later, I did try one and decided that it tasted rather like burnt custard.

BREAKS FROM ROUTINE

During our stay in Malaysia, we hoped to see more of the country, so when Arthur had leave we decided to visit the island of Penang. A long drive took us through jungle, rubber and palm oil plantations. At one stage, we crossed a river by pontoon bridge and arrived on the island by ferry. There is now a bridge from the mainland but ferryboats still sail across.

In Penang, there are beautiful beaches and interesting places to visit which included a ride up Penang Hill on the funicular railway. Halfway up the hill, we had to change trains as each only reaches the midpoint.

From the hill looking over to the mainland, the views were breathtaking. At the top of the hill stands a beautiful temple known as the Kek Lok Si Temple or the Pagoda of one hundred thousand Buddhas. The white walls of the temple contrast with the blue skies and each niche contains a Buddha. Around the temple are other buildings and a pond where turtles swim. As we watched, a monk came to show us a tiny turtle that fitted into Arthur's hand.

Here are two poems about these incidents.

IN AN EASTERN TEMPLE

(Kek Lok Si, the Temple of one hundred thousand Buddhas, Penang)

White latticed walls reflect unclouded skies,
Far distant mountains shimmer in the haze.
And here one hundred thousand Buddhas gaze
in silence, from the niche each occupies,
staring across the hills, from painted eyes.
While in the temple, through the passing days,
saffron-robed monks instruct in Buddha's ways,
as in this place all doubt and discord dies.

Tranquillity extends through every space,
for here the fleeting hours seem motionless,
and all earth's troubles vanish in the mists.
Unmoved, each enigmatic, sculptured face
of the Lord Buddha, stays expressionless
and only peace and harmony exists.

THE TEMPLE TREASURE

In the courtyards of an eastern temple,
Deep silent pools reflect the cloudless skies.
Mirrored pagodas shimmer in the water,
Their colours bright to Occidental eyes.   .

A saffron robed monk pauses by the pool,
smiling shows the reason for his pleasure.
The tiny turtle nestling in his hand
prized more than gold, it is the temple's treasure.

This little symbol of longevity
stands on the threshold of a hundred years.
Time to develop, grow and live its days,
and worlds could change before it disappears.

It waits, indifferent, inscrutable,
like Buddha, shows no feeling on its face.
what does it know of sorrow or of pain?
Secluded here, in this monastic place.

Once more, I stand beside the temple pools,
The sky above, reflected here below
holds in its heights and depths, infinity,
and secrets that our world may never know.

There was so much to see in Penang, in another temple an imposing reclining Buddha about thirty metres in length drew our attention. The robes, covered in gold shone brightly and there were smaller shrines of other Buddhas placed in this temple. Everything was painted in bright clear colours.

We found the Snake temple particularly fascinating for many snakes, mainly pit vipers, live in the temple. Some were coiled on the altar tables and are supposed to be made inoffensive and drowsy by the smell of incense. They were still rather frightening and like everyone else, we kept our distance. There was also a huge python but this was kept caged, even so, most people felt it best not to get too close.

The beaches in Penang were unspoilt and it was a pleasure to walk along them. I felt sad when I heard how this area was also devastated by the Tsunami in December two-thousand and four.

Too soon we had to return to the mainland and normal duties but these sights were something to remember.

When we had been in Malaysia about eighteen months, we were given a break to the Cameron Highlands for Rest and Recuperation, (R&R). To get there, we had to drive up a very steep road with many hair-pin bends as the road wound higher up the mountain. Being high in the hills, the climate there was much cooler, so much so that we needed blankets at night. Previously in Tampin we only needed a sheet to cover us and had been glad of the ceiling fan which kept us cool.

During the day, we went for long walks among the surrounding hills. On a visit to a tea plantation, we were shown the stages of tea production beginning with picking the leaves to the final packaging.

The hillsides had been terraced so that vegetables and fruit could be grown. Strawberries were produced here too but did not have the flavour of English grown ones. Roses were grown in an abundance of varieties and were a pleasure to see. There was a profusion of exotic butterflies but it was sad to see these pinned in picture frames for sale.

We visited a small village built on stilts on the hillside where some of the indigenous Malay people lived. It was interesting to see the villagers who demonstrated their blowpipes. Some of the men in the party tried to use them but not nearly as well as the natives.

This change of scenery was enjoyable and refreshing with plenty of opportunities for photography to enjoy on our return to Tampin.

Some months later, Arthur was again due some leave and we visited Penang once more and spent a pleasant time visiting the places we had seen before and were well worth another visit.

LIFE IN TAMPIN

As I was at work every morning, I was kept busy but most afternoons were free. It could be pleasant to sit in a shady part of the garden, which by now was flourishing. Plants grew quickly in the humid atmosphere and as it rained practically every day, it was almost possible to see them grow.

One day the garden boy brought something to show us that looked like a green log which he planted in the garden. Soon we saw a leaf sprouting up which over the next weeks became a small banana tree. It was not long before a flower appeared and as this grew, we saw the beginning of banana fruits. These bananas grew quickly and it was not long before we enjoyed eating them. Later, he brought some more of these 'logs' which he planted in another part of the garden where in time they grew into a small 'plantation'. Unfortunately, we left before these bore fruit. I hoped that whoever came to live in the bungalow would enjoy them.

Once the banana has borne fruit, the plant dies but if the trunk is chopped into pieces, each portion will grow. Another day he planted a piece of wood that to our amazement quickly grew into a large papaya tree whose fruits grew as large as the marrows we grow in England.

Some afternoons were not peaceful as we could hear trees being felled not far away in the jungle. The sound of chain saws, and the crashes of the trees as they hit the ground were not pleasant.

There was no set monsoon season but it rained almost every day and this came down in a deluge so anyone outside could be soaked in a few minutes. When sitting in the garden, it was possible to hear the sound of rain falling in the jungle on Tampin Hill. This acted like an early warning system giving us time to collect toys, chairs and cushions and take them into the house before the rain reached us. The rain did not last long and when the sun returned, steam could be seen rising over the jungle trees.

During monsoon times, the rain could become heavy and visibility was poor especially at night. One afternoon, I had to take the car to Seremban, thirty miles away for a check and left James behind with the amah. I was glad I did this for being late leaving the town, on the way back it began to rain and this soon became very heavy. It was not a pleasant drive as lightening streaked across the sky and thunder roared above. Even with the windscreen wipers at full speed, it was almost impossible to see the road in front and I still had several miles to go. To pull onto the verge at the side of the road might mean the car becoming bogged down on the soft ground so there was no alternative but to keep driving. Changing down to a low gear, I drove very slowly watching carefully for any hazards ahead. I had heard that once an army Land Rover had run into a water buffalo, which was lying in the road. Apparently, after this incident, the buffalo got up and walked away but the vehicle had to be towed back to camp. With this in mind, I was glad when at last the rain eased and I was able to return home without incident.

James hated the rain falling on his head but for some reason always refused to wear a hat. Even on the hottest day with the sun blazing down, somehow, he always managed to get rid of his sun hat. Despite this, probably because his hair was thick, he did not come to any harm. The sun bleached his hair until it was so fair it became almost white.

One day we noticed an elderly Indian woman walking past our

gate with a small flock of goats. These fed on the sparse grass and weeds that grew along the roadside. James insisted that we should go outside to see her which pleased her very much. She asked for a drink of water which James carried carefully to her in a plastic cup. After this, he always shouted, "friend," when he saw her and asked for the gate to be opened for him to run and greet her.

Once each week, our rubbish bins were emptied by the local refuse collectors. They carried a large basket into which they emptied the bin, spilling quite a lot of the rubbish over the garden.

Another visitor was the 'dhobi wallah' who collected Arthur's khaki uniform and brought it back immaculately washed and ironed. The barber came to cut the men's hair very expertly and neatly. Because it was such a novelty, James was happy to have his haircut too and sat on a chair in the porch while this was done. The price as with many things in Malaysia was very reasonable.

Some afternoons we went to Malacca and looked round the old town where there were many interesting buildings and streets. Many of the houses in the residential areas were built on stilts and had ornate carving around the doors and windows. One shop we liked to visit was called the 'Cold Storage' shop which, as its name implies, was quite cold owing to the deep freezers and refrigerators. A smaller shop, belonging to the same family was situated not far from the camp in Tampin, we were able to buy several commodities there including dried milk, which reconstituted into a passable drink and was useful for cooking.

A favourite walk was to the Malacca River where boats were loaded and unloaded. There were many Chinese people here and it was interesting to see them carrying huge baskets on a long pole across their shoulders. Some of the fishing boats were filled with ice before sailing away, which we guessed, was to keep the fish they caught fresh.

There were many old Dutch buildings in Malacca not far from the waterfront where it was pleasant to walk especially at sunset and see the last red rays reflected in the water. Across the straits lay Indonesia but, everything seemed peaceful where we stood.

In the town, there was a variety of shops selling an assortment of goods. A Chinese dressmaker was able to make dresses using a picture from a magazine as a guide. The selection of reasonably priced materials she produced made it even more difficult to choose.

Vegetables and fruit were bought in the local market although we were able to grow some, such as tomatoes and okra, ourselves. Even though the soil in the garden seemed quite poor, we managed to grow a pineapple. Everything grew well because there was always plenty of moisture due to the monsoon rains. As in Germany, the NAAFI sold a good variety of necessities and by shopping there we were able to eat quite well.

Here too, the wives ran a thrift shop which most found useful as the children outgrew their clothes very quickly. I had difficulty in finding shoes for James as those in his size were very hard and heavy and suitable for a much older child. A shop in Tampin sold English sandals which he found were more comfortable. At home though, he rarely wore shoes, preferring to run barefoot around the house and garden. Because his feet grew quickly, he often needed new sandals; his used ones which were almost new went to the thrift shop where one of the other mothers bought them as they fitted her daughter perfectly.

Our time in Malaysia was coming to an end and Breda wrote to say she had been promoted to Major and posted to Nepal. When she arrived there almost all the senior staff were sick and in addition to nursing them, she had to take charge. Although always full of fun, I knew she would be capable of the serious business of running a hospital.

Our time in Malaysia was almost over and Arthur was once again to go to Arborfield on a course before rejoining the Regiment in

Anglesey. There was quite a lot of packing to do in large wooden boxes that would go by sea. I spent hours painting them with our new address and then packing them with our possessions. James was reluctant to see his tricycle taken away although we told him it would be waiting for him in England. Not quite four, he did not want to part with this favourite toy so we promised to buy him a new one in England. He agreed to keep it until we left and then give it to one of his friends.

RETURN TO ENGLAND

READING

Arriving in England early one morning in March nineteen-sixty we were greeted by a bitterly cold wind as we walked out of the airport. We were glad to reach the hotel we had booked for a few nights to allow us to become acclimatised.

With several weeks leave before Arthur's course began we again needed somewhere to live until we were allocated an Army quarter. In our warmest clothes, we ventured out into the cold London streets. Once again, our destination was Reading, and there we found a small bed and breakfast hotel suitable for a few days while looking for something more permanent.

We needed a place to live for several weeks or even longer so once again we went to an estate agent. There we were advised to find a place on the coast; as at that time of year, before the holiday season, it was easier to find a short-term booking. This suggestion seemed good and the estate agent found us a two bed-roomed flat at quite a reasonable rent in Bognor Regis.

Now with somewhere to live, we collected the car which had been shipped from Malaysia and a few days later we moved ourselves and luggage to Bognor. We were now able to drive around and see the area, enjoying a few sunny days. My parents were eager to see us so we decided to drive up to the Midlands on James' fourth birthday, April fourteenth.

Waking early that morning, when we looked out we saw a thick covering of snow everywhere. Rather than disappoint anyone we set out through the wintry landscape. The snow was quite deep in places yet by the time we had reached Oxford, it had completely disappeared. The rest of the journey north was in sunshine and uneventful. Naturally my parents were pleased to see us and show us round the bungalow they had moved into not long before.

While we were in Reading, James had seen someone riding a small scooter and decided he would rather have one of these instead of a bicycle. We bought one for his birthday and this gave him plenty of exercise.

Soon the time came for Arthur to commence the course at Arborfield where we were given a house straightaway and were able to settle in quickly.

We made friends with the people around us and James was delighted when a place was found for him at a nearby Nursery School. He settled in and found new friends, in particular one little boy of four who rode a two wheeled bicycle. Soon James decided this would be his new skill and with help from Steven who lived a few doors away, learned to ride.

The following spring, James started at the school in the village soon after his fifth birthday, He went into his classroom quite happily but I returned home feeling lost without him and hoping he would be all right. When I collected him later, it was to find he had enjoyed his first day at school and had settled happily making even more friends.

We stayed in Arborfield for about a year and as our time there drew to a close, Arthur rejoined the Twelfth Regiment in Anglesey. Army quarters were in short supply at Ty Croes where the Regiment was stationed but we were able to find a flat in Rhosnieger on the coast not far away.

By this time we were used to a variety of different homes so although this flat was not ideal, as it was only temporary, we did not mind and treated our time there rather like a holiday. James attended the school there for a few weeks and joined in their sports day but found it more difficult than the school near Arborfield as most of the children spoke Welsh.

In the summer months, Anglesey was a pleasant place with enjoyable walks in the area around or along the beach gathering shells. One day a plane from RAF Valley crashed into the sea. The pilot was able to eject and was not injured in the incident. There was great excitement as crowds collected to watch a helicopter crew inspect the damage before the plane was recovered leaving nothing to show where it had been.

Another night there was a severe storm and in the morning, we saw debris along the roads. A small fishing boat was thrown up onto some rocks not far from where we were staying, all things of interest to a five-year-old child.

We were in Anglesey for about three months and then before Arthur's army service ended, he was sent to Stevenage in the south of England on a course for several months. Because of this, we decided to look for a house in Burnley which was where we hoped to eventually settle down.

At that time, houses were not difficult to find and before long a suitable one was found. Two weeks before Arthur was due to leave Anglesey, we moved to Burnley in September nineteen-sixty seven. Having been in army quarters or furnished accommodation previously, we had little in the way of furniture so shopping for essentials was a priority.

Once settled in, a school had to be found for James and as we were now civilians, a doctor. The school was convenient with a good bus service if the weather was poor; and James settled in well.

Once these things had been settled, I did some decorating in the house and bought more furniture. After this, I found I had very little to do and began to look for part time work that would fit in with school hours. An advertisement in the local paper, stated that the Prestige works wanted part time women to pack cutlery. The hours seemed suitable as I could start work as soon as James had gone to school and be free to meet him in the afternoon. I applied to work there in the mornings and was able to start the following week. Depending on the type of cutlery to be packed, it was not always as easy as packing biscuits had been. Nevertheless, it was good to be busy and there was some extra money for necessities and treats.

THE MATERNITY UNIT

In the autumn of the following year, a new Maternity Hospital was opened not far from where we were living and there was to be an open day the following Saturday.

"I'd like to have a look round," I said to Arthur who was home that weekend.

"Why not?" he said. "Perhaps they might need more staff."

The hospital looked very streamlined with new labour wards and an operating theatre. The four-bedded wards looked airy and there were several single rooms and isolation wards. As I walked round, I spied a woman in a grey uniform and noticed by her badge that she was Miss Cox, the Matron.

This was my opportunity and as no one else was near I spoke to her.

"You must be very pleased to have this new unit," I said.

"Yes, it will be lovely to work here when we open officially next week," she answered.

"Are you likely to need any more midwives?" I asked diffidently.

"Why? Are you a midwife?"

"Yes," I said. "I've not been long in Burnley but I did most of my training in Birmingham and I spent three years in the army working mainly in Maternity Units."

"Then write to me as soon as you can," she said, "tell me everything you have done and I will let you know if I can take you."

As soon as I returned home, I began my letter. Fortunately, I had references from the MO I'd worked with in Malaysia and the colonel of the Regiment so I enclosed copies.

By return of post, an answer came to tell me to attend the sewing room to be measured for a uniform and to start there a week later. I was to work for five days from nine until two each day. These hours would suit me very well for I could take James to the school bus and then walk the short distance to the hospital which was close by.

On reporting for duty, Miss Cox sent me to Jackson Ward, the GP Unit. Arriving there, I found I was not the only new member of staff for the Sister and other midwives had just arrived from a small hospital in a nearby town. This meant that they knew as little as I did about the new hospital but the arrival of some patients meant we had to set to work quickly.

Working on a GP Unit was rather similar to being on the district except that we had all the facilities of a well-equipped hospital ready to hand. Just as on district, some doctors wanted to deliver their own patients or be present at the birth. Others wanted only to be informed when their patients were admitted. The system worked very well and soon everyone settled into a routine. The other members of staff were friendly and we got on well together.

Patients who came into the ward in labour were examined and whichever midwife admitted them stayed in charge of that particular patient. When it was thought they would soon be ready to deliver, the patient was taken to the delivery suite on the ground floor where the midwife stayed with them until the baby had arrived safely. Midwives and patients seemed very happy with this arrangement.

Before long, everyone had settled down and then the staff from another small maternity unit joined us. Now there were more staff, after a few weeks, I was sent to work in the Delivery Suite where all new patients apart from those booked with their GP were admitted and assessed. If at this stage, labour was not established they might be sent to one of the antenatal wards, of which there were three, or returned home.

The hospital was a training school for midwives, so there were always new students wanting to witness births. Other students needed to be supervised and encouraged as they performed their first or subsequent deliveries. The Sister in charge was very experienced and good at assessing one's capabilities.

I enjoyed the work there though I knew it would not be long before being moved to one of the other wards. Before this, however, I was told I must go on the refresher course that all midwives were required to do every five years. As it happened, I was able to get a place on a course in Leeds that would last for a week and was not too far away. This created a problem as Arthur was on another course and unable to get leave. My mother said she would come and look after James and as he lived near, Arthur's father said he would keep an eye on things.

Having been out of the country, the refresher course enabled me to learn new ideas to bring me up to date. Pregnancy and labour had not changed but there were new methods and equipment to be shown. Although enjoying the week, it was good to leave on the Friday evening and return home.

The following Monday, I found I had been moved to one of the 'lying in' wards. These wards, of which there were three in addition to the GP ward, were quite busy as at that time, mothers were kept in for several days. In many ways, this was a good system, especially for mothers with first babies.

Although on these wards, one had little to do with the actual delivery, the period after the birth could be difficult and mothers needed constant reassurance. Some who had stitches found these could be most uncomfortable and painful and were relieved once these were removed. Breast-feeding following a Caesarean birth could be difficult and painful and I was able to help these mothers by assisting them to lie on one side whilst feeding. If the mother was uncomfortable, this communicated to the infant who would not feed.

One day the consultant came to see one of the patients who complained that he had been wrong about the sex of her baby.

"You said this would be a girl but I got another boy," she told him. The consultant did not have an answer for this but it reminded me of a story I had once heard. A consultant at a well-known hospital used to boast that he could always tell the sex of a baby the first time he saw a mother in the antenatal clinic. He then wrote something in the patient's notes; on visiting the ward after she had delivered, the mother would either say he was correct in telling the sex of her baby or tell him he had been wrong.

That's impossible," he would say, "You must have misunderstood me."

"No! I'm sure you said I would have a boy and it's a girl."

"But look, I wrote it in your notes he would say, here it is." Sure enough he had written a 'G' in the notes.

His method was to write in pencil, the opposite in the notes to what he told the patient. If she said he had been right, there was no need to show anything, if she said he was wrong, it was in her notes to show he had been correct.

On one occasion, we had a diabetic patient in one of the small side wards behind the nurse's station. She was due for discharge one morning but checking to see if she was ready, I could see that something was wrong. In the excitement of going home, she had not eaten much breakfast and she was about to go into a hypoglycaemic coma. This is when the level of insulin in the blood is too high and immediate steps need to be taken to rectify this.

I called one of the other staff to ring the doctor and inform him whilst I managed to get her to drink some glucose in water. This seemed to revive her a little and when the doctor arrived, he gave her an intravenous injection of glucose after which she recovered quickly. It is always amazing how quickly a diabetic patient can return to normality with this treatment. Unfortunately, the doctor decided she must stay in hospital for another night to make sure she did not have another of these episodes. Next morning, I made sure she had eaten sufficient breakfast and had been given some glucose tablets before she left the ward.

Apart from incidents such as this, the work on these wards was routine and was without the added interest of getting to know the patients during delivery. From this point of view, the smaller maternity units such as some of those in the Army are better. In units such as these, the midwife meets the patient during the pregnancy and even if not available to deliver the baby, she is already known to the patient.

I know the midwives who had been transferred from the small hospitals missed this aspect of care although most of them stayed permanently on the GP unit. When training, it is good for the student to see all aspects of treatment, but both patient and midwife do prefer to have some continuity of relationship in care.

Soon I found out how busy the antenatal clinic at this hospital could be as my next move was to work there. This was before there were such things as scans and foetal heart monitors. Each patient had her blood pressure taken, was weighed and examined by the midwife before seeing the doctor. The booking clinics were especially busy and I understood why one patient likened the whole process to be 'like a cattle market.'

There was little chance to get to know any of the mothers really well in the short time I worked in the clinic but soon, I was moved back to the labour ward. The senior sister in overall charge was good to work under but I found that because, being part time, my position as a Staff Nurse made some of the Sisters treat me as if I had no previous experience. On the whole, I did enjoy working there but began to want something more challenging.

SOMETHING DIFFERENT

HEALTH VISITING

During this time, Arthur had completed his service in the army and had found work with an engineering firm in Burnley. As he needed the car for going to and from work, we decided to buy another for me to use. We settled on a small Fiat five-hundred or Topolina (little mouse) as they were nicknamed, although when we bought this car we did not know how useful it would prove to be.

As part of my student nurse training, I'd had a day with a health visitor and thought it would be interesting to work in this area. Then one day, on looking through the local newspaper, I noticed an advertisement for nurses to train as Health Visitors and pointed this out to Arthur.

"I've always been interested in work on the district," I said.

"Then why not ring and ask for an application form?" he said.

I rang the Health Department, not expecting to hear anything for a few days but on the following afternoon when coming off duty, the telephone was ringing as I arrived home. I lifted the receiver wondering who it might be.

"Is that Mrs. Baxter?"

"Yes?" I replied.

This is the Chief Nursing Officer for Burnley Health Services. I believe you are interested in Health Visitor Training?"

"Yes, I am." I replied.

"Can you come and see me tomorrow afternoon at my office on Nicholas Street?"

"Yes," I said.

"Bring details of your previous training and any references you have with you," she went on to say before ending the call.

The following day the interview with Miss O'Brien seemed to go well.

"All Health Visitor training takes place at The Institute of Technology in Bolton and you will have to go there for an interview with the Principle Tutor."

It was not long before an appointment arrived and I drove to Bolton one morning. I found myself with several other would be Health Visitors being interviewed, answering a questionnaire and filling in forms.

We were informed that the next course would start in September and take a year to complete. During the course we would be paid by our Local Authorities and also receive travelling expenses. The pay was better than I received as a Staff Nurse and would increase once I completed the course.

Having a car made it much easier to commute to Bolton every day when told I had been accepted. Before the course started, I was invited to meet another student from Burnley who had been accepted. Pauline lived in Burnley and was eager to travel with me so we made arrangements for the journey.

Our first day was taken up with registration and getting to know others on the course and our tutors.

"I want you to give an account of what you have done to date and a resumé of why you wanted to come on this course," the head tutor told us.

The following day, at the end of these short talks we knew something more about each other. Then lectures began in earnest with book lists and homework.

The weeks rushed by, then one afternoon we met our Field Work

Instructors who were experienced Health Visitors. About every two months, we would spend one week with them and have several families to visit and report on. We also attended clinics and visited schools with our instructor.

Pauline and I went to different Health Centres in Blackburn but as these were not too far apart, we could still travel together. Our Instructors introduced us to the families we would visit so we could then put into practice what we had learned in the lecture room. Later, we were told, we would write comprehensive case studies about our work with these families which would be used as part of our assessment.

During the course, we also went for a week on what was known as alternative practice. This had to be in a different type of area than the one where we would eventually work. As my work would be in a town, the rural area of Skipton was chosen which was not too far away.

Another coincidence occurred when I arrived in Skipton, to be shown round the Health Centre and introduced to the other staff. To my surprise, Cynthia with whom I had worked in Birmingham was working there. Unfortunately we did not see much of each other as we both had our own work. During this placement, I visited clinics at various hospitals in the area and was introduced to some of the other agencies with whom I would work as a Health Visitor.

Meanwhile, in Junior school, James was having difficulty with reading although he seemed bright and knowledgeable on his school subjects. I had queried this with his teachers, being sure he was dyslexic, but when seen by the school psychologist, I was told this was not what was wrong. Despite this assurance, I was not convinced but we were able to find a remedial teacher who gave James tuition twice weekly and this helped him improve his reading.

The weeks sped by to the end of the course and exams. Before qualifying, we had three months supervised practice in the areas where we would work.

In Burnley we joined the practices to which we had been allocated. This enabled me to get to know the practice doctors, district nurses and midwives attached to these practices. Best of all I would be working with families, schools and elderly people and helping them with problems.

Although we did not meet with the aggression that seems commonplace today, it was not always easy. There were some awkward moments for when one knocked on a door, it was impossible to know what sort of reception waited there.

One day, I went to visit a child who had just had an infectious illness which meant she was off school for a while. It was necessary to do this kind of visit to make sure that there were no after effects from the illness. To my surprise, a large burly man opened the door.

"What do you want?" he asked.

"I am the health visitor attached to Julie's school," I said, "I've come to see how she is and if there are any problems after her illness."

"She's fine now," he said and was about to shut the door.

"Could I come in for a moment to speak to her about school?" I asked.

This I was allowed to do and after talking to the child and her father, was able to leave feeling that he was happy about my visit and was not interfering in their lives. Later in my work, we were given identity cards but at that stage, the only means of proving identity was our official diary.

Having worked in the hospital and in the ante-natal clinic, I was not a complete stranger to many of the families I had to visit. Also, after working on the practice for a while, people got to know me and I rarely had other problems.

One of the most interesting parts of the work was visiting new babies on or near their tenth day. This was to assess their progress and find out whether the mother was having difficulties with feeding or needed help with other problems. Another reason for this visit was to do a small blood test, (the scriver test) on the baby to check for certain abnormalities. To do this, the baby's heel had to be pricked and in the early days, blood was obtained onto a special paper and sent to the laboratory. Later, a small capillary tube was used and this was much more efficient. It meant that other tests could also be done.

Recently there has been research on whether babies feel pain. I myself have never had any doubts about this though I do not know of the intensity they may feel. Is it because something unpleasant is happening or is it really painful? Remembering one infant I am sure that babies have memories of pain. He had needed several heel pricks for blood samples in hospital because of jaundice and when I swabbed his heel prior to taking blood, he screamed and kicked causing difficulty in obtaining the sample. Did he remember the pain and was protesting against it? I do remember when working in hospital, all newborn infants were given an injection of Vitamin K; their response was usually loud and indignant.

When at last, we received our exam results and Certificates it was something of an anticlimax to have finished studying. When Pauline told me of a course for the Diploma in Nursing at Burnley College, I said I would join her. This could lead to a course to become a Clinical Teacher and Arthur was encouraging so I enrolled. There were three subjects, Physiology, Psychology and Nursing. The lectures were given by a local GP who was very knowledgeable and made difficult subjects interesting.

There was a lot to learn and the exams were hard, I passed in two subjects but was referred in Physiology which I retook the following year. Unfortunately, by then, I had enrolled on an Open University Degree Course that started the following January. Pauline had passed and gone on to study for the Clinical Teachers Course.

It was quite hard to revise for the Diploma and take the Foundation

Course for the OU but somehow, I managed and passed in both exams. There were many more years of study before I would get a degree but later in the year, I went to a Summer School in Stirling and enjoyed gaining knowledge and meeting other mature students.

My colleagues at work were helpful and always ready with advice when asked. With quite a wide variety of families, there was always something to discuss and in the early days, it was good to call on their expertise. At the same time they were always willing to help out at a clinic or visit a new baby if someone was on holiday.

VARIETY

Sometimes the unexpected could happen as it did when a colleague asked me to visit a new baby while she was away on holiday.

"You'd better take some Wellington boots with you," she said. "Because the parents live in a caravan across a field which is always muddy."

The following week I set out in a fine drizzle and having found the correct field gate, put on my Wellingtons and gingerly set off. The ground had been churned up to a deep sludge by the action of farm animals. I clutched my bag firmly and carefully made my way through the mud to where I could see the roof of a caravan above the hedge in the next field.

Reaching my destination, I stretched up to knock on the door. After several minutes, I knocked again and this time, the door was opened by a tall burly red-faced man who glowered down at me.

"What do you want?" he asked.

"I'm a Health Visitor," I explained. "I'm here in place of Miss Edwards as she's on holiday. May I come in?"

He glanced down at my muddy boots but before he could object, I said, "Of course, I'll take my boots off and leave them outside."

"All right then, come in."

I slipped my feet out of the boots and followed him into the caravan where a woman sat nursing a baby.

"Hello," I said, "I think Miss Edwards told you I would be coming today."

"Yes she did. She said something about a blood test for the baby. Have you got to do it today?"

"Nobody told me about a blood test. What do you have to do it for?" His tone was belligerent and I felt that this was a difficult situation as I began to explain.

"Although your baby looks very well and healthy, there are some conditions that only show up as they get older. This blood test will show us if he has one of those conditions which we can then treat early."

While I was explaining this, I was getting out the equipment I would need.

"All right ," he said but he kept his eyes fixed firmly on me.

"May I wash my hands?" I asked.

He did not reply so taking this as a 'yes', I went to the small sink and washed my hands. After this, I examined the baby and asked his mother about his progress and if she had any problems with feeding.

Having done this, the mother removed the baby's bootee and I swabbed the infant's heel and took the blood hoping that all would be well and nothing would go wrong. Luckily, I had no trouble in obtaining sufficient blood for the test and apart from a sudden cry, the baby settled down quietly.

"It will take about a week before the results come back and I'm sure Miss Edwards will let you know on her next visit." I said.

During this time, the hostility from the father was much less and he took me to the door and held my bag while I put on my Wellington boots again.

This was one of the worst receptions I ever had for although husbands were often present; the antagonism I'd felt at that particular visit was not repeated. Many of them were more interested in why the tests were done and what happened if a positive result was obtained.

On one occasion, one baby was not thriving well and was seen by the paediatrician who diagnosed the rare metabolic disorder of galactasaemia, This occurs when the baby is unable to covert the sugar in milk, (galactose) into glucose. Once diagnosed, the baby was given special milk and began to thrive. The mother was determined to do everything she could to help her baby. As the child grew older she methodically checked the ingredients of all the food she gave to her little girl, even writing to the manufacturers to check. It was surprising how many foods contained galactose, often in small amounts but sufficient to make a child with this condition quite ill.

The little girl made extremely good progress which I am sure was due to the care given by the mother. When a second baby arrived, tests were done to check whether this baby had also inherited the condition but luckily she had not. Not long after this, the family left the area but I did hear that both children were well and the oldest girl had settled well into school and making good progress.

Most mothers tended to be anxious about the progress of their baby and this often showed in the way they handed their son or daughter. If the baby was fretful and cried a lot, I was able to reassure them and show them how to soothe the child. Talking to an infant in a soft low voice often induced the baby to stop crying and listen and then, often fall asleep.

During this time, my Open University studies were continuing although at times it could be difficult. I found that some of the knowledge gained was useful to me in understanding the people I met. In the evenings, James, who now, at Senior School, had homework sat with me as we worked together.

Passing the end of year exams enabled students to go on to another course. Most of my subjects were in Psychology and these meant attending a Summer School held at Universities in different parts of the country.

Having looked after babies with pyloric stenosis in the past, I suspected this when a mother reported that her baby girl was bringing back most of her feeds. This was not her first baby so I was sure the mother's feeding techniques were satisfactory. The GP was inclined to think that this mother was too fussy but with perseverance, he eventually admitted the baby to hospital. With treatment, the condition was resolved without an operation and Katie began to put on weight to everyone's relief.

For some reason, it is mainly boys who develop this condition which usually starts in a previously healthy infant when about a month old.

Time passed by very quickly and when one of my colleagues retired, I took over her practice. The head of this practice was a woman doctor who was good to work with and always ready to see any clients with problems. She had the ability of being able to diagnose a medical condition well before any tests proved that she was correct. She referred two children to the paediatrician at the early onset of leukaemia which was treated quickly and both made good progress.

In addition to babies and young children, there were many elderly people to visit to check whether they were managing or might be eligible for extra benefits. On occasion, they had been sent application forms to fill in and were completely baffled by them. It was not surprising for these forms were quite complicated with many of the questions difficult to understand. Even after sending the form to the appropriate department, it could be weeks before there were results.

Once I visited an elderly lady with a terminal illness who was cared for by her retired niece who lived some distance away. An application was made for additional help and for this, a doctor visited her. Like many elderly people do, she got up early and with difficulty dressed herself in preparation. When the doctor arrived he asked only a few questions and thinking she did not need any help, he left. The outcome was that she was not granted any extra money which would have been a great help to her. Sadly, she only lived a few weeks longer and I wished I had known her longer when perhaps I could have helped more.

Another elderly lady I visited lived alone with her delightful black cat who like its mistress was quite a character. Even at nearly ninety, Annie still baked cakes for children in the neighbourhood and was very popular. When younger, Annie had sold what were called 'fents' (remnants of material of all sorts) at the market in York . She had many regular customers there for the material was cheap and could be utilised to make a variety of clothing especially in the days after the war.

How I enjoyed listening to her tales of her younger days, some of which were rather sad! During the war, she had been engaged to a captain in the Merchant Navy and often travelled to Liverpool to meet him off his ship. The guard on the dock gate soon got to know her and if Captain Bill's ship was in whistled, 'She's a lassie from Lancashire' and then Annie knew it was all right to wait for him. There was a sad end to this story for his ship was sunk and Captain Bill never returned.

We became good friends and after I retired, I often visited Annie to listen to her reminiscing. Like many of the elderly people I visited who lived alone, she was always glad to have someone to listen to her stories. Not long after this, Annie became ill and was taken to hospital where I visited her until she died and went to meet Captain Bill at last.

Working on the district could have difficulties but getting to know the families and be able to advise them could be rewarding. Every Wednesday afternoon, I held a baby clinic at the Health Centre which was quite well attended. Sometimes it was not only mothers and babies who came but others knowing I would be there came to discuss a problem with me.

By visiting families regularly, it could be easier to detect any problems as they arose and give the right advice to the parents. With their permission, I was able to refer them to the GP who could then examine the baby or child appropriately. Often a parent would be worried but did not like to trouble the doctor about this; a health visitor who knew the child after visiting several times could give details of the problem to the GP.

Once, when I was away, another Health visitor went to see a new baby for me. "Don't be surprised if she won't let you in!" I was told. It did not seem an ideal situation when later, with some trepidation I knocked on the door. The response when it was opened, was not surprising,

"What do you want?" the tone was curt and not at all welcoming.

"I've come to introduce myself as your Health Visitor," I said. "I'm sorry I was not able to come last week. I've now got the result of baby Natalie's blood test."

"You'd better come in then," was the curt reply.

The room, though sparsely furnished was clean and neat, the baby, dressed in warm clothes was asleep.

"How has she been?" I asked.

"She's a little horror," her mother replied. The softened look on her face belied the words as she looked down at the baby. She turned to me. "What about the blood test? I'm not going to have it done again!"

"The blood test was fine," I reassured her. "How is she feeding?"

"She's a greedy monster. I've just made a brew, want one?"

I realised that to refuse would not endear me so I accepted and soon we were discussing the baby, her first, quite amicably. From her attitude, I gathered Jan had come up against authority before and was not going to take kindly to being told what to do. Nevertheless, she listened to whatever I had to say and perhaps acted on my advice for her children, (later she had three in total) were all cared for and healthy.

Quite often when visiting Jan, I would be greeted with an abrupt, "Oh it's you! Come in."

This was her way and though brusque, she never refused to invite me in. Some years later, I was outside a supermarket in a town some distance away, when a voice called. I turned to see Jan behind me.

"I'm living here now," she said and proceeded to tell me how the children were getting on. Natalie the eldest had left school and was working, the two others were still at school.

Quite often in town, I would be called or spoken to by my old clients who were glad to tell me how well their families were progressing.

One extremely windy autumn afternoon, I went to visit a family who live on an estate built on a hillside. I left my car, now a slightly larger Fiat 126 in a bay at right angles to the road and went to the house. On my return; the car was missing! This couldn't be true, I thought rubbing my eyes and despite the wind that had intensified, hurried to the road side.

Had it been stolen? But who would want to steal a small nondescript car?

A little way down the road, a woman was struggling to walk although the wind seemed to be doing its best to prevent her.

"Have you lost a car?" she asked as she drew near enough to get her breath.

"Yes! I have!" I replied.

"A small blue one? It's down there." She said and struggled on her way.

Having no idea about what I might find, I made my way down the road, the wind blowing so hard, I could hardly keep upright.

Just past a bend in the road, I saw it. Somehow it had come to rest against a concrete garden post but to do so, it had run across the pavement a grass verge and over a small, foot high wall. I looked at it and saw that the back bumper was dented but miraculously, the rear lights were intact.

Wondering what to do as I stood looking at it, a man came out of the house into the garden.

"Is it your car?" he asked.

"Yes," I said. "I'll have to get a garage to move it."

"Wait a moment," he said as a lorry drove down the road to stop nearby.

Two men got out and came across to look.

"Can you do anything?" the first man asked.

"No problem," they said and after I had released the hand brake, proceeded to lift the car up and push it back onto the road.

It seemed that the wind must have lifted it in such a way that the brakes were ineffective and pushed it backwards down the road. With a feeling of relief I thanked them, they climbed back into the lorry and with a wave, drove away. Very carefully, I drove back to the office where a strong cup of tea restored my equilibrium. Later, taking the car to the garage to be checked, no damage was found apart from the dent in the bumper.

Some time later, we heard that the strong gales that day had even blown Morecambe pier away.

When he heard about this incident, Arthur said he thought it was time I had a larger heavier car which would not be moved by the wind so easily.

This prompted me to go back to the garage where I had bought the small car. The salesman was pleased to sell me something larger and as I drove away, I thought, the ill wind certainly did him some good.

SCHOOL WORK

In addition to working with babies and elderly people, the health visitors had work in schools, which included giving advice to parents and teachers and assisting the School Doctor at Medical Examinations. In one school, the buildings were in very poor condition. No repairs were carried out because a new school was being built so Medicals had to be conducted in a draughty room where several bowls and buckets caught rain from the roof. The teachers were pleased when they moved, finding pleasure in working in a new school.

Part of the work in schools was to give some basic instruction in how the body works and for this; I went on a course one day each week. This was for the City and Guilds Teaching in Higher Education Certificate but our work in Junior Schools was assessed as part of it.

At the same time, I was continuing to study for my degree and managing to pass the exams each year. Although James was making good progress in practical subjects, his reading and writing were still poor. One evening, we watched a programme about dyslexia on television together.

Afterwards James said, "That's just like me."

"Would you like to know for sure?" I asked.

"I think I would."

I was able to arrange for him to be seen by a psychologist at Lancaster University where what I had suspected, was confirmed.

Rather than being upset by this, James was glad to know that his difficulties had a reason.

"I'm not thick," he said. "The teachers were wrong."

He loved art and as his hobby was bird watching was good at drawing birds. The art teacher said he would have no difficulty in passing 'O' level art.

"His only fault," he told me, "although not really a fault, is that he spends so much time in attention to detail. He must have everything exactly right."

James himself wanted to improve and perhaps go to university and worked hard to gain the appropriate 'A' levels. We tried to encourage him as much as possible; he had failed English 'O' levels several times and so he decided to go to Burnley College for a term and this time passed.

Being able to draw well, I said to him "When you take the exams, if you can draw a diagram, make it as accurate as you can and label it carefully. That way, the examiner will see that you know your subject."

I knew he was worried about the 'A' level exams and the week before the results were due, he decided to go for a few days to watch birds on the coast. He arrived home at the end of the week and on the following morning he received a letter from Preston Polytechnic. They were offering him a place on their Applied Biology Course to start in September. It was only then that he told us he should have been at school for the results, the previous day.

"You must have done reasonably well in Biology," I said "to be offered this place. Go into school on Monday and find out for sure."

This he did and had passed in Biology 'A' level and also passed in Human Biology at 'O' level, a subject he had only studied for one year. If his results were better, he had hoped to go to Lancaster University to study Biology but unless he stayed at school and tried to obtain another 'A' level this was out of the question.

"You have two choices," we told him, "You can stay at school another year or go to the Polytechnic. Whatever you decide to do, we will help you all we can."

He decided to go to Preston, spent two successful and happy years there, and in his last term was offered a place at Lancaster. At the end of the course, he had passed in all subjects and gained Merits in all his practical work. This meant that he could now accept a place a Lancaster to read Ecology, a subject in which he had become interested while at Preston.

It was a proud moment when we went to Preston Guild Hall to watch him collect his Diploma later that year.

In my studies with the Open University I had now gained a Bachelor of Arts degree and decided to go on to third level courses to make this a BA Honours. During his first summer vacation from university, James decided to join an archaeological 'dig' at Crickley Hill near Cheltenham. He enjoyed this trip; especially getting to know the other students and said he would like to go again the following year.

During that summer, I had a Summer School at Sussex University and James decided to go with me and stay at Youth Hostels close to Beachy Head and do some serious bird watching. We drove down together, James driving part of the way and arrived in Brighton in the afternoon. I arranged to pick him up at the end of the course and drive to my brother George's house in Stansted for the weekend. This made a pleasant break before the long drive home.

Back at home, James was preparing for his second year and I returned to work again. There were new babies to visit and problems in schools. One of these was recurrent head lice and in the absence of the school-nurse, I was often asked to check the children's hair. Despite all the advice given to parents on prevention, it was still a problem.

One Friday afternoon, I had just returned to the office when the telephone rang. It was one of my mothers, Rachel, in great distress because someone from Social Services had just been to see her. Apparently someone had reported that one of her children had cigarette burns on his body and the social worker had insisted on examining all the children. This mother was known to me as someone who kept her home spick and span and children well cared for and always neatly dressed. Neither she or her husband smoked so to be accused of burning her children must have been an insult.

A short time later I was on my way to see her and found her very distressed.

"Who could have done this?" she wept.

I tried to console her and when I left much later, she was less agitated.

Soon after this the family moved to the next town and I did not see as much of her as things seemed better.

Therefore, it was surprising, just before Christmas, nineteen eight-three to receive a telephone call from Rachel. She sounded upset so I visited her as soon as possible. She was living in temporary accommodation in a grimy terraced house in one of the poorer areas of town.

"I don't know what to do," she wailed as she mopped her eyes.

"Tell me what the trouble is?" I asked.

In between sobs, she told me what had happened.

It appeared that the whole family had gone to visit relatives in Pakistan, and this had gone quite well. On return however, her husband had been arrested at the airport, leaving them to find their way back to Burnley with hardly any money.

Apparently while they were away, he had sold the house and everything in it so now the family had nothing. They could only stay in the house they were in for a few days but she had been promised rented property when they had to leave. Meantime they had very little money and no furniture.

I promised to do what I could to help and decided to ask if any of my friends could assist. One of them knew the minister of a local church would know where help might be found. He and his wife found beds for the children and someone else was able to give other items such as clothing. When they moved, things looked much better.

Telling James about this later, he said, "What about Christmas? Will they have any presents?"

I told him that although Moslems did not keep Christmas I had seen that many of them had decorated trees in their houses.

"Well then, let's give them ours," he said and proceeded to dismantle the decorations from the tree. With sweets and fruit, we made our way to the house and put up the tree, which delighted the children and their mother who now felt much happier. My poem, 'Christmases Remembered,' recalls this incident.

Later, the family moved again and I lost touch with them. Rachel had told me that she had become reconciled with her parents who were Jewish and had not approved of their daughter's marriage. Perhaps she returned to them with the children. The husband was sent to prison for drug trafficking and I do not know whether he returned to his family.

Working with families often meant sharing not only their joys but also their sadness. One young mother with a toddler son was delighted when she and her mother were given a refurbished council house and settled in happily. Then, one morning when her mother had not long gone to work, the house caught fire. The mother and child were rescued but were so badly affected by the fire, they both died later in hospital. The loss of her daughter and grandson was so hard for the mother that she could not return to the house even after it had been renovated.

Most of the families were working class with little money to spare but could be very ingenious. Visiting one such family, at Christmas, I saw that the mother had collected several large twigs that had fallen from the trees in a nearby park. These she had painted white and gold, then hung baubles and presents for the children making it look very effective; the children were very happy to play with the small gifts.

Later, I went to visit a toddler whose mother told me she was worried about her older child.

"She had a bad cold but she doesn't seem to be getting better," she said.

"I'm sure the GP will be glad to check her and perhaps give you some medicine to help," I said.

The problem was worse than we thought for Rachel was in the early stages of Leukaemia and prompt admission to hospital allowed treatment to be given and this led to a successful outcome.

Not long after this, another child was also diagnosed with Leukaemia and due to modern treatment; he too made a good recovery.

It was most important to keep up to date with new methods and treatments so heath visitors had to attend refresher courses. I found that my Open University higher-level courses in Psychology were very useful in understanding the people with whom I worked. One of my courses was on Cognitive Development in young children and the acquisition of speech. One of the mothers was pleased to help with the case study for which I had chosen her child. She was happy for me to visit in my own time to discuss the progress her small son was making and to keep a record of new words.

This course helped me to gain an Honours degree and membership of the British Psychology Association.

James came home for the Easter break and we celebrated his birthday by buying him a small car. He said he needed some transport, as he had to travel a distance to some woods where he was doing a study on small mammals. It would also be useful for travelling to the university as he now had digs in Morecambe. As he set off again and we waved goodbye we could not know that we would never see him again.

At work, as usual we were kept busy and now I was looking forward to the summer holidays. I had thought that this would be the last holiday James would spend at home for he had said he wanted to work with VSO, (Voluntary Service Overseas.)

On the evening of June the twentieth, I was alone as Arthur had gone out, when a police car drew up outside. The news they brought was devastating for it was to tell me that James had died in a road accident that same evening. We found out later that he had been on his way to check on the traps he had set to collect information for his project. For a while we were numb with shock but there were others to tell and that had to be done, however difficult.

While at home, James had received telephone calls from his friends and one he told me was called Susan who was in her final year at St Catherine's College in Liverpool. I knew she must be told but I had no address other than the name of the college. Having found the number, I rang there only to be told she had completed her course and returned home. The college would not give me her number but said they would pass a message for her to ring me.

Susan had no idea what had happened and I think telling her was one of the hardest things I have ever had to do. She was very upset but we arranged for her to come and stay with us so that she could be at the funeral. It was very hard for her for they had been at the beginning of what might have been a good relationship. Over the next years, I met her quite often and became good friends with her. Several years later, she met someone else and married but we still keep in touch.

LIFE GOES ON

If we knew what was going to happen to us in the future, it might be difficult to carry on. Yet despite the difficulties, there is only one thing to do and that is to resume the everyday routine. It is hard when the future seems empty and hopes and dreams have been shattered.

For me, going back to work did help for even though James had been away most of the time, the house still seemed empty although at times it seemed as if some part of him was still close. During his life, he painted and sketched many pictures of birds and because of these, something of his remained.

My colleagues at work helped through this difficult time, being understanding and helpful. Without actually saying a great deal, they conveyed their sympathy and were always ready to help.

Looking back, I wonder how we got through the next months and years. Losing someone so close is devastating yet it does help to understand other people better. I found my clients and friends, who having read the news, did not need to say anything for their sympathy was conveyed in other ways. In time, the pain of loss eases and the happy times are remembered with thankfulness.

In the words of a poem I read once, 'It is better to have loved and lost than never have loved at all.'

At that time, the practice had a varied clientele living in different types of housing. It was not easy for many of them as wages were low and the type of work many could do did not fit in easily with family commitments. Quite a lot of the women did an evening shift at some of the factories but this meant leaving home as soon as their husband arrived from work to be there for the children. This was not always good for their relationships and meant that often marriages broke down,

This type of existence was stressful but by letting them talk over their worries with me often seemed to help them to find their own solutions. My work was interesting and varied as each day brought fresh problems for me to try and resolve. Building up a relationship with the families I visited could be difficult but in time, I found that I was welcomed. It was helpful to me as listening to others helped me come to terms with my own problems.

One morning, I visited a young couple in a nearby town with a new baby. At one of my follow up visits, the mother told me she was soon going back to work and was worried about leaving the baby. Both parents worked and had arranged to do alternate shifts which would mean there would be always someone at home to care for the baby.

Unfortunately this was not the best of ways to develop the relationship between the couple as their time together was likely to be very limited. A mother returning to work when the baby was only six weeks old could tire easily. In addition, a baby needing attention during the night did not help. Those mothers who had their own mother or an aunt who could help with the baby were fortunate for the number of day minders was limited besides being expensive.

I remember visiting one family where the mother worked full time and the father who had been made redundant, looked after the toddler. He called himself a 'house husband' but from what I could see, all he did was look after the child and his wife had to cook and clean when she returned home. These are some of the hidden problems that many hard working people have to overcome.

At one time, I visited a single mother who had five children, all under five, who had difficulty if one was ill. One of the receptionists in surgery was annoyed as this mother was always asking for home visits from the GP. When it was pointed out to her that to bring one sick child could be difficult but this mother had to get five ready and bring them all which was not easy especially when the weather was bad and the only transport was a pram.

Many of our clients were Asian, some of whom did not speak English but quite often had a friend who did and who came in to interpret but in time I was able to describe, what was needed and they seemed to understand. This was made clear when after visiting one woman who had problems with sterilising the baby's bottles and teats, I met her older daughter in the street who, just home from school, was on her way to buy the correct sterilising fluid for her mother.

Visiting these families, they always insisted on making me a cup of tea; as part of their culture, food or drink should always be offered to a visitor. Their method of making tea was quite different to the English way; first water was boiled in a saucepan on the stove, then tea leaves were thrown in. The water was boiled for a few more minutes, then milk and sugar added before being poured into cups. The resulting concoction was not always pleasant to drink but the provider was delighted when it had been accepted and drunk.

I found the method of making tea in Burnley was quite different to the way we made it at home.

Often when visiting a family, I would be asked "D'you want a brew?"

Before receiving an answer, the kettle was switched on and a spoonful of tea put into a mug or beaker, milk added and stirred. Before tea bags were used, this often resulted in a mouthful of tealeaves causing the recipient to choke. Yet I often found that when sitting and talking with a client over a cup of tea more was learned about their problems and advice was more likely to be acted on. A hasty visit often gave the wrong impression so that rather than seeing me as an intruder, I became a friend in whom they could confide knowing I would only pass on information with their permission. It did not take a lot more time and the information gained while observing the children was well worth extra minutes.

One afternoon in clinic, one of the mothers told me she had heard that Doctor P. was retiring soon.

"Is it true?" she asked.

"I don't know but I'll see if I can find out. I said.

Later that week I asked the doctor in she was thinking of retiring."

"Oh no." she said, "I intend to work as long as I can."

Sadly, not very long following this, after only quite a short illness she died. This well loved GP was more like a friend to all her patients; it was a terrible blow to everyone who knew her.

One of the pleasant elements of my job was to visit nursery schools and I always enjoyed seeing how the young children were encouraged to learn. Not long after this, the time came for me to retire from the full time work I had loved. Things were beginning to alter and I felt that although I had enjoyed working with families, I was concerned about the way our work was being changed and did not feel at all happy about this.

One of my commitments was with a nursery not far from my home and on retiring, the head teacher asked me to become a Governor. This involvement was different but just as interesting and lasted for several years. To see a shy child who had probably never been away from home become engrossed in new activities and make friends was rewarding for the teachers and nursery nurses.

In addition to this, since being a small child, I had written stories and poetry but with study and work, these had to be put on one side. Now, I had time for this and joined a writers' group and having interest in young children, wrote several stories for the nursery group.

It was only then I realised that learning never ends for this new craft required hard work and readiness to rewrite and adjust the written words. It has been hard at times but enjoyable and I shall continue as long as I can.

Looking back over my years as a nurse and midwife, it has been hard work but most rewarding. The decision to take those first steps on the road into nursing and beyond, was almost certainly the best thing I ever did.

GLOSSARY

Ante-partum haemorrhage – *bleeding before the birth of the baby.*

Balkan Beam - *a framework fitted over a bed to which pulleys could apply traction to align fractures and support injured limbs.*

Flying squad, *an obstetric team called for an obstetric emergency.*

Foetus, *the unborn baby,*

Foetal heart *the unborn baby's heat beat.*

Gas and Air machine, *this delivers a mixture of 50% nitrous oxide and 50% air.*

Galactasaemia,- *an error of metabolism where there is inability to convert galactose (milk sugar) to glucose. Treatment is to eliminate all foods containing galactose or lactose from the diet.*

Left lateral position, - *the mother lies on her left side for delivery of the baby.*

Occiput anterior - *the occiput is the back of the head. The position is anterior when the occiput is pointing towards the front.*

Pethidine, - *a drug used in labour for the relief of pain.*

Pinard's stethoscope - *a small trumpet shaped instrument for listening to the foetal heart beat.*

Placenta, - *the afterbirth.*

Placenta praevia - *the placenta lies over the cervix and can cause severe blood loss.*

Pre-eclampsia - *a raised blood pressure in pregnancy associated with oedema of hands, face and ankles. The urine may contain albumin. If not treated can lead to eclampsia , convulsions in the mother and death of the foetus.*

Thomas splint - *used to apply traction for a fractured femur and is used with a Balkan Beam bed.*

Uterus – *the womb.*

Uterine fundus – *the top of the uterus, furthest from the cervix.*